Jamie Ireland, Freedom's Champion

To the father of James and Mark

J. C. Ballew

1927–1964

Jamie Ireland

FREEDOM'S CHAMPION

William N. McElrath

Illustrated by
William Moyers

BROADMAN PRESS
Nashville, Tennessee

© 1964 · BROADMAN PRESS
Nashville, Tennessee
All rights reserved.

424–084

Dewey Decimal Number: B (or 92)
Library of Congress Catalog Card Number 64–18777
Printed in the United States of America
5.AL64KSP

Contents

Freedom—1762

You know from history books that many of the people who settled America came in order to find freedom of religion.

But you may have learned also that some of the very people who came to America seeking freedom for themselves were slow about giving such freedom to others.

Lawrence Southwick, America's first skilled glassmaker, was fined because he was a Quaker, and his children were almost sold as slaves to pay the debt. Dr. John Clarke and his friends moved from Massachusetts because church officers threatened them with heavy fines. Obadiah Holmes's back was furrowed by a three-corded whip because he helped to hold a religious service in the home of an elderly blind man; the authorities called the service "illegal."

And in the colony of Virginia, in the years between the French and Indian War and the American Revolution, there was only one official established church.

The government used tax money, collected from all the people, to support that church—to build its houses of worship and to pay its ministers.

If a Virginian wanted to worship God in some church other than the official one, he had to get special written permission and obey troublesome rules.

And he still had to pay taxes for the established church.

There were a few men who dared to stand up and say, "All churches ought to be under the same laws. No church should get special benefits. And no government should have authority over churches."

James Ireland was one of those men. He was willing to suffer persecution and even go to prison for standing true to his beliefs.

Fortunately James Ireland left a written record of his life.

The story, as Ireland told it, included many thrills, many surprises. He was a dauntless man, made for adventures. And he discovered while still young that finding and following Jesus Christ is the greatest of all adventures.

His out-of-breath narrative ranged from whaling voyages in Arctic seas to threats of death in a Virginia county jail. It included pranks and fights in school, when he was a handsome Scottish boy in old Edinburgh, known to his classmates as Jamie Ireland. . . .

1
Wartime in Edinburgh

Jamie Ireland sauntered down the High Street in Edinburgh, silver shoe buckles shining in the morning sun. He whistled the skipping strains of "The Piper of Dundee"; staid Scottish merchants turned on the way to their shops to look at the short, slender fourteen-year-old.

A fife and drum interrupted Jamie's solo. Redcoat soldiers marched past. One squad was urging on three men whose dingy tatters had once been proud uniforms of France.

I wonder how it feels to be a prisoner, mused the boy. He made a face as he thought of moldy bread and water, of barred windows and locked doors.

"Captives from the Indian wars?" shouted Jamie at the last rank of Redcoats.

"Nay, not these, lad. They were shipped from the American colonies, not India," answered the one soldier who seemed to notice.

"Did they not fight the red Indians, then?" persisted Jamie, catching step with the soldier.

" 'Tis not likely. Most of the red men fight on the French side, not ours."

For one glowing moment Jamie marched on with the soldiers. He was Wolfe storming the cliffs of Quebec; he was Clive routing the French from the Carnatic coast of India.

Then he dropped behind, his eyes wistful and far away. His shoulders drooped. *Why dream of being a fighting soldier that gets to see the great world, when Father will not even let me try a boxing match at school?*

With slower steps he turned and walked down the Canongate. He glanced up as he passed John Knox's house. His eyes traced the inscription over the quaint front door—put there two centuries ago by the great preacher himself, so Jamie's father said:

LUFE GOD ABOVE AND YOUR NICHBOUR AS YOURSELF

My neighbor might well be any man, thought Jamie. *At least, so says the minister in kirk on the Lord's Day. But how can I love those that tempt me to fight?*

"Hey, Jamie!" David Erskine's merry voice jarred him out of his thoughts. "What a long face you make!"

" 'Tis nothing, nothing!" snapped Jamie. Then he flashed a smile to show his friend that he was not really angry.

"Why worry on your way to school?" teased David. "Surely your marks are high enough."

Jamie slapped his hand down hard on the Latin book he carried. "Same old tale, Davie," he grumbled. "My father still thinks it wrong to fight, and he will not hear to it."

"Not even when you are challenged to a boxing match?"

Jamie shook his head. "He thinks a lad reared in the Church of Scotland should 'live peaceably with all men,' as the Bible says."

David shrugged. "I'd expect that from *my* father, him being a minister. And he warns me straight enough to be no brawler, no ruffian. But dropping my fists when another lad offers to strike—why, that's something else again."

Jamie nodded. "I think 'tis really something more than religion. You don't remember my elder brother, George, do you?"

David shook his head.

"George and I were playing when we were wee bairns, and Geordie fell and broke his arm. It would not heal, and the doctor said, 'Cut it off,' but he died before they could. I think that ever since, my mother has worried about me getting hurt, and my father listens to her."

"Ah, well, he does not forbid you to run." David jostled Jamie and grinned. "And *run* is the word, now, or else we're late to school!"

Soles clacked on cobblestones and echoed from smoke-stained brick fronts of three-story buildings as the two teen-agers raced down the Canongate.

Panting, they drew up at the doorstep of the school, with Jamie the victor by six feet. He grinned at David as both boys mopped their faces and tried to calm their breathing before entering.

"Have you finished your assignment?" asked Jamie as they started up the long stairs.

"Not quite," confessed the other boy. "I can get it before he makes us recite, though."

Into the huge schoolroom Jamie walked, ducking his head in what passed for a bow in the direction of the schoolmaster. David did the same. They hurried to their seats, whipped open their books, and began to practice reading their Latin in loud undertones. So did half a hundred other scholars who had already arrived. The room sounded like the wasp's nest that Jamie had poked from a tree in Pentland Hills last summer.

The schoolmaster, a stately figure topped by a large powdered wig, left his desk and began to stroll up and down the side aisles. This exercise, as Jamie well knew, would not long continue. Soon he would bark a word of command:

"Silence!"

The next word might well be "Ireland!" or "Erskine!" and Jamie or David would be required to stand, march forward, and give an account of his preparation for the day's lesson.

Past Jamie's seat on the aisle stalked the majestic professor. Jamie could not resist his impulse. Up he jumped and stepped to the teacher's side, so that the teacher only half turned to face him.

"Please, kind sir," he began, "I cannot find the meaning for this word."

The schoolmaster curtly explained, and continued his walk toward the front of the room. But behind him he left a small whitish cloud floating in midair, and stifled snickers from several boys. For Jamie, using his large Latin book as a shield, had reached around the teacher's back with his other hand and tapped several puffs of powder out of the longest curl of that magnificent wig!

Luckily for Jamie, the cloud had faded into unnoticeable wisps when the schoolmaster turned at the front of the aisle. He raised an eyebrow at the muffled laughter, but said nothing and resumed his stroll.

Jamie looked from side to side. David and several others nodded their encouragement.

Jamie tapped puffs of powder from the teacher's wig.

He waited again till the master had reached the back of the room, turned, and passed his seat on the way forward. Then the boy half stood and swung his leg in a nimble kicking motion toward the teacher's departing back.

This time the snickers were too loud. The schoolmaster wheeled around and spotted Jamie just as he dropped back into his seat.

Sternly the professor charged down the aisle, his eyebrows linking to make a capital V. Clutching Jamie's ear, he marched him toward the front of the room, where the rod hung in silent warning.

Several painful minutes later, Jamie eased down again in his place.

Another unpleasant morning at school was under way.

During recess David shook his head in sympathy. "Too bad he had to catch you. 'Twas beginning to be the best performance of the year!"

Jamie rubbed the seat of his trousers. "Let the old man beat me for playing the fool all he pleases; he'll never get to beat me for playing the dunce."

"Come along, lads!" cried another boy.

"What's to do, Hastings?" asked David.

"Wheesht! We're too near the school," warned Hastings, dropping his bass voice to a whisper and further shielding his words behind a hairy hand. "You know well enough what's to do when we get past yonder hedge."

Jamie dropped his head. He also knew what went on behind the hedge. Wars and rumors of wars had roused the boys of Edinburgh to fighting pitch. Too young to battle Indians in Canada or French in India, they felt they must test their manhood somehow. Secret boxing matches helped them to work off their coltish bursts of energy.

"You can go along with them if you like, Davie," muttered Jamie.

"What's the matter?" minced Hastings in mocking tones. "Can you clown like a lad but not fight like a man?"

Jamie clenched his fists, spun on his heel, and walked away, but not before he heard the larger boy fling at his back the word he had come to dread:

"Coward!"

'Tis no fair, he moped. *Even if the French invade us, as some folk talk, I suppose Father will say, "Jamie, remember you're son to a Scottish gentleman. Strike no blow in anger."*

As always, Jamie was one of the first out of the schoolroom when class was dismissed that afternoon. In spite of his quickness to learn, he did not really like school—or schoolmasters. They interfered too much with his freedom.

Back up the Canongate he trudged, up the High Street, up to the tall house with its weather-beaten sign:

JAMES IRELAND
COUNSELOR-AT-LAW

The boy paused to tilt his head back and stare at the battlements of Edinburgh Castle on the heights of Castle Rock. He turned and looked northward toward Leith, wishing he had time to hike down and see tall ships from all the world riding at anchor. Then he heaved a long breath and dashed up the steps into the house, knowing that Mother would expect him to be washed and neat when he came to the table.

Meals were strangely quiet in the Ireland house, considering that there were six children. But Mrs. Ireland kept her standards of taste and fashion high. No child could eat with his parents until he had learned his manners.

Of course Jamie had earned his promotion from the table in the servants' hall several years ago. Sometimes he wondered whether it was worth the trouble. For instance, at supper several weeks later . . .

"Laddie, laddie," cooed his mother. "Must you eat so fast?"

"I'm hungry, Mother," the boy appealed.

"Aye, one would think we had starved you a week

before we set this mutton in front of you," she continued. "Do try to eat properly."

When it was not his mother correcting him, it was his father talking about business. And if he let his mind wander . . .

"Pay attention, Jamie! How can you expect to practice law someday like your father and grandfather—God rest his soul!—if ye give no heed when I unfold legal matters?"

"I beg your pardon, sire," mumbled Jamie, suddenly recalled from brooding again over Hastings' insults. The older lad had been teasing him repeatedly, after once discovering that he would not fight.

"As I was saying," continued Mr. Ireland, "I find the need of my law clerk this very night, to finish preparation of the Duncan case. Haste you when you have eaten, to his house just to the north of the Lawnmarket, and fetch him back here again."

"Mr. Ireland!" cried Mother. "Will ye send a bairn out now, with night fast coming on?"

Father met Jamie's steady gaze. " 'Tis no long journey, lady, and no mere bairn I send. The lad is quick and strong, and he knows the way well—do ye not?"

"That I do, sire," replied Jamie. He stuffed in the last few bites of mutton even faster than before, ignoring his mother's sounds of distress.

Glad for an excuse to get outdoors again, Jamie

hurried through the hall and down the stone steps.

Frost nipped his nose and the crisp air seemed to sting as he breathed in great gulps of it. He began to whistle "The Wee Cooper of Fife," bobbing his head to the rhythm.

"Hoot, hoot!" grated a husky voice in the twilight. "Who be this young laird that gangs so fast?"

Jamie squinted to see a dirty-faced boy about his own age. Three others, the same size or smaller, stood in a ragged line behind him.

"Be he a excaped prisoner, capting?" piped the smallest boy.

"Nay, worse," exclaimed the "captain." "He be a deserter!"

Jamie realized what the little group represented. Poor boys of the streets often tried to imitate the squads of soldiers that crisscrossed Edinburgh every day. But Jamie had no time for war games now.

"Stand aside," he ordered. "I have an important errand yonder side of the Lawnmarket."

" 'An important errand,' says he," mocked the leader. "Likely sellin' millinery secrets to the Frenchy-frogs, that be his errand."

Jamie clenched his fists. "For the last time, clear the way. I am Counselor Ireland's son, bound to fetch his law clerk."

"High and mighty!" retorted the boy with the sooty

face. "We'll just see about that, won't we, ma braw sojers?"

The other three, armed with heavy sticks carried as muskets, gave a high-pitched cheer and started closing in on Jamie.

He felt his heart thump. "I—I want no fight," he stammered. "I must not!"

"Then come along wi' ye to the guardhouse!" cried the boy-captain, jerking Jamie by the elbow.

This was too much. Jamie snatched one of the sticks and began to flail in every direction.

The smallest boy fled at once. The others swung sticks and fists, and several blows from the leader made Jamie yelp with pain. Yet, it was only a few seconds before the whole "army" retreated pell-mell, leaving him victor in the battle.

Jamie dropped his stick and tenderly patted a bruise on his left cheek. Beneath the fuzz—turning dark and stiff in recent weeks—his flesh felt sore to touch.

"Well done, my brave lad!"

It was a deep, familiar voice. Jamie pivoted to see the approaching figure of Mr. McLennan, the merchant who lived next door to the Irelands.

Instinctively, Jamie turned and ran. *Did he recognize me in the dark? Will he tell? What will Father say?* The questions in his mind seemed to pound louder than his feet on the pavement.

2

Champion of the Ring

Jamie and the summoned law clerk climbed the Irelands' steps. The clerk immediately turned into the large
front room that served as a law office. Jamie, not wishing
to meet his father just then, continued down the dark hall
toward the inside stairs.

As he passed the closed door of a back parlor, he
stopped and blinked. That voice—he couldn't be mistak-
ing it. It was Mr. McLennan's again.

As well be killed for a wolf as a lamb, Jamie decided,
no matter what Father or the minister might think. He
bent forward to listen at the keyhole.

". . . And to make short shrift of it, he put the whole
mob of them to their heels as bonnily as ever I see."

Mr. Ireland cleared his throat.

(*Now it's coming,* thought the boy in the hall.)

"I know that James has a quick temper, and a fighting spirit that needs no encouragement," stated the father.

(*He never calls me James save when he is angry,* Jamie reflected.)

"But, for all that," continued Mr. Ireland, "I am better pleased to hear how he acted, than if he had run away like a coward."

Jamie straightened up like the ends of a stick chopped in the middle.

Thinking he heard his father coming to the door, he eased on upstairs, trying to digest and understand this strange piece of good news. He compared it mentally with his father's usual teachings, and became more and more confused.

Should I ask him what he meant? he wondered.

(*And admit that you were a sneak?* suggested his conscience.)

Jamie shook his head as he flung coat, shirt, and trousers over a chair, shook off his shoes, wriggled into a cold nightshirt, and dived for his bed.

He still had not managed to sort out all of his thoughts several weeks later, when he and David again meandered out of their schoolroom at recess.

"They're boxing behind the hedge today," announced David softly. "Will ye come and watch again?"

Jamie frowned and sucked in his cheeks. Then—

" 'Lay on, Macduff!' " He drew an imaginary sword

and lunged at David, who whirled around and led the way toward the hedge.

The first match was already under way. Hastings and another tall lad had squared off and were eyeing each other, waiting for an opening. Suddenly the other boy swung, and Hastings pounded him repeatedly in response.

"Shame!" shrilled one of the spectators.

"You must not hit above the breath, Hastings," cried another.

"Aye, what will happen to us all if the master sees blood or bruises?"

"Hoot!" scoffed the broad-shouldered boxer. "I did no more than graze him; look you, there is no mark."

The other boy, though, was clutching his eye. One of his cronies advised him to go and splash cold water on it at once, lest the telltale black swelling begin.

"Next?" sneered Hastings, jabbing the air with his bare fists.

Another boy entered the makeshift ring, and the fighting went on.

"Hastings still seems to be the champion," explained David, "although one or two have made him call it a draw."

During a pause between rounds, Hastings noticed Jamie standing beside David. "Ah," he purred, "his majesty comes to review the troops today. Attention!

"Watch him close, Jamie!" urged David.

Present arms, men, to the lad who will not fight!"

Even in the chill breeze of early spring, Jamie felt his cheeks starting to burn.

"Come now," Hastings teased again, "will ye not dare to fight, and me with one hand tied behind my back?"

Snickers began to circle the group—this time *at* Jamie, not *with* him.

"Guard my book, Davie," Jamie suddenly heard himself saying. "I'll trade blows with this blustering wind!"

"Well!" snorted Hastings in mock wonder. "Who would have believed it! Haste, lads, and bind my arm."

Two or three boys, who seemed to jump at Hastings' every suggestion, knotted together two handkerchiefs and managed to tie his left hand behind his back.

"Watch him close, Jamie!" urged David.

Hastings leered and poked with his one hard-knuckled fist. "Come, my bonny one! I'll knock that 'blustering wind' out o' your lungs!"

Jamie had watched the others box often enough that he did not feel entirely at a loss. This fact, plus Jamie's naturally quick eye and nimble body, soon gave the handicapped champion more than he had bargained for.

"Stand still, ye will-o'-the-wisp, and fight like a man!" he roared.

But Jamie continued to skip back and forth, dodging all but the most harmless blows, and landing a few well-aimed punches himself that made Hastings wince.

At last, bellowing like a bull calf, the larger boy ripped the handkerchiefs that bound his left arm.

"Shame, shame!"

"You threw down the challenge, Hastings."

"Will you give over?"

Jamie tilted up his chin. "Be not too hard on him, lads," he crowed. "Perhaps he did not know who he was fighting. I'll box him with two hands apiece!"

Hastings sullenly jerked off the shreds of the handkerchiefs and began to stalk his prey. Jamie soon found he had talked himself in deep, for that burly left arm now blocked most of his light pokes. But he doggedly kept dancing—now to the left, now to the right, now a sudden duck as Hastings' fist whizzed through his hair.

Once the larger boy again broke rules and struck Jamie on the nose. Tears burned his eyes, but he forced himself to keep both fists between himself and his foe. Even when he felt a warm trickle on his upper lip, he did not forget to watch and dodge.

Now Hastings' breathing was becoming more labored. His heavier body could not track Jamie's dancing feet without weariness beginning to show.

At last Jamie saw his chance. Hastings' arms were a split second slow to return after trying a double jab at Jamie's chest. The smaller boy drove in his fist with all his strength, just above the belt buckle.

Hastings doubled forward, wheezing. Two of his friends caught and supported him.

Jamie leaned against David's shoulder, heaving for breath. Many hands pounded his back in congratulation, as David awkwardly dabbed away at the blood from his nose.

"The master will never see," he assured Jamie.

Now Hastings had recovered enough of his wind to straighten up—with help. He glared at Jamie, but at the same time licked his lips and fingered his throat as if he felt a bit sick.

"I see a few rags of those handkerchiefs yet," gasped Jamie. "Shall we tie *my* hand, and to it again?"

A chorus of laughter and hurrahs broke from the group.

Hastings spat. He and his little band of followers turned away without a word.

Thus began the career of Jamie Ireland, champion boxer of the Latin School in Edinburgh. He did not win every match during that school year and the next; Hastings, fighting with the fury of a grudge, knocked him dizzy once or twice. But beyond question he won more often than any other scholar.

David's father, the minister, overheard his son telling of Jamie's exploits. That was how it happened that Mr.

Ireland called, "James!" one spring afternoon more than twelve months later as Jamie passed the door to the law office.

"Yes, sire?" Jamie stepped inside and waited.

"Sit ye down." Mr. Ireland shuffled several legal papers and laid them aside. "Mr. Erskine says you have been a-fighting. Tell me the truth; is it so?"

Jamie nodded. "But sire, I thought—well, I thought—"

"Thought what, lad? Make a clean breast of it."

And so at length Jamie told his father of the statement made to Mr. McLennan which he had heard by eavesdropping many months before.

"I thought, sire," he concluded, "that you must have changed your mind, and would not care that I fought."

"That was one case, and this another." Mr. Ireland shook his head. "Why did you not come to me next morning and ask me straight what I meant?"

Jamie looked down at the worn carpet.

"Now, understand this, if you can, my lad. I mind it not that you put to flight those young ruffians. Thus far you got my meaning right."

Jamie rubbed the back of his neck. "Then why have you always said I must 'live peaceably with all men'?"

"You quote the book of Romans well," admitted the father. "But there is more to that verse: 'If it be possible, as much as lieth in you, live peaceably with all men.' I think it was not possible in the case of the street ruffians—not if you were to retain your freedom."

Jamie nodded and grinned.

"But—" Mr. Ireland held up a finger. "There is another verse or two in Holy Writ that better explains my feelings. 'Tis found in the book of Ecclesiastes, chapter 3: 'To every thing there is a season, and a time to every purpose under the heaven: a time to keep silence, and a time to speak; a time of war, and a time of peace.' "

Lawyerlike, Mr. Ireland ticked off the separate cases on his fingertips. " 'Twas a time to fight when they barred your way. 'Twas a time to fight, so I hear, when schoolmates blackguarded you with mocking words. But to go on boxing for to make sport—laddie, I do not think that was a time to fight."

Again Jamie nodded. Then he looked up at his father's face—solemn, as the lecture came to an end.

"Try to remember—fight when you must, but always test yourself: 'Is this really a time to fight, or no?' 'Tis all I ask."

"Thank you, sire." The boy rose and turned quickly toward the door.

"And Jamie . . ."

He looked back over his shoulder.

"No more listening at keyholes, do ye hear? 'Tis a legal matter, and I might sue!" A hint of a smile curled the corners of Mr. Ireland's mouth.

"Yes, sire!" Jamie grinned and bolted.

Later, as he lay awake in bed, he thought again about the self-test his father had given him. He chuckled to remember how near it was to the end of school—not just the year, but the five years of his Latin School course. This meant he would have few opportunities now to use the test, and for that he was glad. He suspected that his father's test would keep the rightful champion from entering any more boxing matches behind the hedge.

3
To Sea!

Jamie made the most of his first full day of freedom from school by strolling down to Leith. He walked along the wharves, staring at ships—coasters, men-o'-war with cannons gleaming, tall three-masters that sailed the trade winds to America, pilots' boats that ventured no farther than the mouth of the Firth of Forth. He looked for the four whalers, then remembered that they would no doubt be on their way to Greenland at this springtime season.

Longshoremen trundled a cartload of cheeses past him. Two fisher-boys scarcely older than he struggled to hoist a salty-smelling barrel onto a donkey wagon. A ship's officer strutted by, his regimentals spotless, his gold-laced hat and sheathed sword reflecting glints of sunlight.

Something about the officer's walk made Jamie turn to

glance at him again. The officer also turned and looked him full in the face.

Jamie gasped. "Davie!"

David Erskine's laugh echoed from the stalls of the fish market. Drawing his sword with a grand gesture, he cried, "On guard, Laird of Ireland!"

Jamie jiggled his head as if to clear his vision. "What's all this?"

"Why, 'tis the garb of a midshipman in His Royal Majesty's Navy," chuckled David, sliding his sword into place. "Do ye not like it?"

Jamie gulped and nodded. "And are you really a midshipman?"

"I dare not be seen in this, were I not," replied the other sixteen-year-old. "Did you not remember I would go into the navy straight after school was out?"

"Aye, but I did not realize you would be an officer."

"Well, now, a midshipman is *barely* an officer," admitted David. "I'll have much to learn, no doubt, in yon man-o'-war. But a lad of proper family finds it not hard to become a midshipman, if he choose."

The conversation soon came to an end, for David had gotten special leave to walk along the dock and impress his friend whom he had spotted from the forecastle of his ship.

Jamie kept seeing that hat and glistening sword, kept smelling the salt-tanged air, kept hearing the groan of hawsers as the wind tugged ships away from the shore. Even that night he dreamed a mixed-up dream in which he, David, and the schoolmaster all slid down an iceberg in pursuit of a boat that was about to leave them behind.

By the end of the week, he had made up his mind. Boldly he knocked on the door of his father's office.

"Come in, come in."

Jamie stepped inside.

"Ah!" Father leaned back in his chair. "If 'tis not young Master Ireland. And what case calls for my counsel today?"

Jamie, grinning, decided to plunge in at once. "The case of a Latin School graduate who wants to go to sea."

"To sea!" Mr. Ireland suddenly sat forward again.

"Yes, sire."

The father frowned and waved his hand toward the shelves of lawbooks. "And what about all this?"

Jamie sucked in his cheeks. "I would not say I never want to be a lawyer, but could I try the sea first?"

Under his father's cross-examination—searching, but not unkind—Jamie explained his yearnings in more detail, especially the way he felt when he met Mr. Midshipman Erskine on the wharf at Leith.

Mr. Ireland fumbled with his waistcoat buttons. Finally he sighed, "Give me some time to think it over, my lad. God forbid that I should make my son into a lawyer if he likes it not; 'tis a hard enough life when a man does. But the sea! Let me turn it about in my mind awhile."

The next few days seemed to pass like turtles crossing the road. Jamie's thoughts were more and more wrapped up in the sea—that great, pitching unknown beyond the mouth of the Firth. By day he stood—even in a cold drizzle—to watch sailors go about their work at Leith. By night he ransacked the family library for tales of the sea, but found few except that thrilling long-ago voyage and shipwreck described in the twenty-seventh chapter of the book of Acts.

More than a week had passed before Father called him into the law office. A man whose tanned face looked vaguely familiar sat in a chair by the window.

"James," began Mr. Ireland, "surely you remember my distant kinsman, Robert Clyde?"

Jamie stammered.

The man with the tanned face came to the rescue as he gripped the boy's hand warmly. "He may or he may not. He and poor Geordie were but wee scudders when last I dropped my anchor in your parlors here."

"Mr. Clyde," continued Jamie's father, "is captain of a coaster that sails for London on the afternoon tide of Tuesday next. He has agreed to take you on as a passenger, to find how the sea agrees with your constitution. What think ye of that, now?"

Jamie almost blurted out his disappointment. A coaster

instead of a tall man-o'-war, and only as a passenger at that!

Then somehow his father's self-test about fighting darted into his mind. Was this a time to fight for what he thought he wanted? After all, he would at least get to see a bit of the ocean. And if it agreed with his constitution, maybe . . .

Forcing a smile, he said at last, "I think 'tis a bonny idea, sire, and I thank you with all my heart."

(*'Tis a bonny lie, too,* warned his conscience; but Jamie found his conscience easier to ignore than it used to be.)

Jamie had thought the days would crawl by again till the next Tuesday. Instead he found them filled to the brim with things to do and thoughts to think.

Mother loaded him down with mountains of good advice, and mountains upon mountains of coats, shirts, trousers, hose, and drawers piled into his trunk.

"You'd think I'm bound for America instead of merely for London!" he protested.

"I've heard the summer climate in London is most uncertain," replied Mother, unperturbed. "Who knows what clothing you may need?"

Jamie managed to cram in two more quick trips down to Leith, where Mr. Clyde's little coaster was taking on the last of her cargo. He grinned to hear that David Erskine's man-o'-war was to convoy the coaster and

several others down to London, providing protection
against French privateers that still roamed the North
Sea.

At last the tide began to rise on Tuesday afternoon.
Jamie leaned over the rail to watch with delight as the
coaster began to lift perceptibly with it. Soon the little
fleet had left behind waving relatives and friends, the
pilot's boat, Burntisland on the port side, even the craggy
peaks of Castle Rock and Arthur's Seat.

And so it was that Jamie Ireland first went to sea.
Really, he never knew whether to count it so or not, for
the coaster scarcely got out of sight of land—either on
that voyage or on the following winter voyage for which
Captain Clyde asked to "borrow" Jamie again. The tiny
ship put in at many a harbor to leave and take on
passengers and cargo, also to buy fresh meat and bread.

Mr. Clyde took special care to see that Jamie was well
supplied with everything he needed. The cabin was
cramped and dimly lit, but Jamie and the youthful first
mate shared with the captain the best of all that was
available.

The second London voyage brought Jamie his first
opportunity to earn money on his own.

Together he and the first mate leaned on the coaster's
rail and watched bargelike lighters nose alongside to
ferry London passengers and cargo ashore. Older members of the crew also scrambled over the ship's side.

The mate looked wistfully after them, then turned his gaze toward the bank of the Thames and frowned.

"Why do ye not go too?" inquired Jamie. "Look you, Mr. Clyde is yet aboard; I thought 'twas only when the captain leaves that the mate must stay."

The husky young man shook his head. "I dare not set foot on yonder shore—not if I expect to see my sweetheart waving her welcome from the pier at Leith."

Now it was Jamie's turn to frown. "I see no connection."

The mate's lips exploded with the words: "The press, lad, the press!"

Seeing that Jamie still looked puzzled, he went on to explain the forcible way that ordinary seamen for British battleships were "recruited" in those cruel days. Any able-bodied man who stepped ashore without a written protection might find himself seized and shipped off to war, willy-nilly. Jamie shuddered at the thought of such loss of liberty.

"And so, ye see, my love might be wed to another and I an old man before ever I see Leith again."

The mate paused, stepped back, and surveyed Jamie's slender frame. "I scarce can think, though," he continued, "that they would notice so slight a lad as you—even with the press being so hot just now. Will ye do my work ashore, then? I'll split the extra pay that would be my due."

And so Jamie found himself feeling important as he stood near the bank of the Thames—receiving cargo, scribbling receipts, and directing longshoremen who piled goods into the warehouse.

Once he saw a little knot of muscular, tarry-handed sailors approaching. From their searching glances in every direction, Jamie decided they must be a press gang. He glided back toward the shadows inside the warehouse door. There he stayed till the seamen disappeared.

A few days later, Jamie again leaned on the coaster's rail and watched sixty hogsheads of sugar being hoisted up from lighters and stored in the hold. Then he heard Captain Clyde shouting to the boatmen: "We must put off for Sheerness on this very tide; else we miss our convoy. The rest of the cargo must wait for the next voyage."

For three fourths of the homeward way, the little coaster met no rougher winds than might be expected in winter months. But as night began to fall opposite Tyne-mouth Bay, a hurricane blustered out of the southwest.

4
Storm and Shoal

"Reef the sails!" yelled the captain above the shriek of the wind. Every pair of hands on board—passengers and crew alike—strained to furl every thread of canvas, so that the gale would find as few surfaces as possible against which to push.

Time and again Jamie found his head entangled in the foresail, and expected the next flap of the yardarm to fling him into the churning water. At last the sails were reefed, the helm was lashed hard-a-lee, and the hatchways were battened down with tarpaulins, bars, and bolts.

Only the captain, the ship's carpenter, and Jamie stayed on deck to finish the job. Everyone else tumbled down the last open hatchway to the comparative safety of the cabin.

Great waves licked across the coaster's deck. As the

night turned blacker, the wind blew harder, driving the little craft farther and farther out to sea. To Jamie, clinging to halyards, rails, or anything else attached at which he could lunge, it seemed the waves were stretching higher than Castle Rock. The aching chill of heavy wet garments sticking to goose-pimpled skin seemed to bite at his very bones.

Dawn found the skies clear. Yet, the rising sun shone on waves and winds as fierce as those of the night before. Spray and spume reflected the sunlight and made the whole world seem spangled with fire.

Jamie scanned the horizon. No man-o'-war was in sight, and only two topmasts showed the probable locations of other ships in the coasting fleet.

As the day wore on, matters grew worse. Breakers tore away the quarter rails, and with them, several bales of nonperishable cargo that had been fastened there.

The ceaseless rocking of the coaster now showed Jamie what a calculated risk had been taken in sailing without a full cargo. Those sixty hogsheads of sugar, riding in the upper part of the hold, all rolled to one side, and the deck began to tilt dizzily.

Leaks were showing up, too. Jamie and the carpenter inched their way aft to work a few strokes on the bilge pump between waves. Jamie found himself in constant peril of sliding down the slope and overboard when he would use both hands on the pump. Finally he tied himself to the double ropes of the shrouds with the lower ends of the main topsail halyards.

As the storm lingered for a second night, Jamie felt like gritting his chattering teeth and howling back at the wind. *If ever I set foot on solid ground again,* he vowed, *you could cut my two ears off before I would venture on the ocean again!*

The tempest had dragged into its thirty-second hour before Jamie could tell that it was lessening. As the wind eased a bit, it also veered around to almost the opposite direction.

"Unlash that helm!" bawled Captain Clyde. " 'Twas hard-a-lee when we fastened it, but look you, now 'tis hard-a-weather!"

With the helm reversed, the makeshift deck crew of three now managed to unfurl the jib and the forestaysail. Thus, little by little, they got the lee side against the battering waves, so that the forces of wind and water were counterbalanced. Soon Jamie hurrahed to hear the sugar hogsheads beginning to roll back into place.

The coaster was nearly righted at daybreak, when the drawn-faced inmates of the cabin began to creep up an opened hatchway to the deck.

Now a new danger threatened. The captain of David's man-o'-war had apparently feared the storm more than he feared the French, and so had deserted the fleet. Fortunately Leith could not be many days away. Mr.

Clyde called for every possible sail, leaks or no leaks, to press on there as soon as possible.

It was afternoon when they sighted their home port. The captain used every trick he had learned in a lifetime to make a last spurt into harbor before sunset.

Jamie felt like cheering when they passed the mouth just as night began to fall. Looking up to the heights of Edinburgh, he could distinctly trace the chimney tops of the High Street along the skyline.

Were those the Irelands' candles flickering in windows to welcome him? Surely they were, or at least the McLennans' next door. *I'll be home in two hours, no more,* he congratulated himself.

Just then he pitched forward to his knees.

"What happened?" he cried.

Captain Clyde swore eloquently. "Fire a signal gun, bosun; we have run her aground."

Jamie groaned.

The pilot seemed to know that Jamie and others were eager to be ashore; in a remarkably short time he climbed aboard from his little boat.

"The tide is due to rise two feet more," he informed the captain. "Throw your topsails aback, and I believe she'll float."

He was right.

"We'll stand a little off to sea," suggested the captain. "If the tide comes in as much as ye say, hoist two lamps in the lighthouse. We'll tack about and stand in for another try."

The pilot's boat disappeared in the gloom. It seemed centuries to Jamie before two flickers of light swayed against the darkness.

Captain Clyde shook his head. "I fear we are too far out now to make it before the ebb tide commences."

"We must not stay here, sir," muttered the mate. "The leaks grow worse."

"Then we'll make for Burntisland," decided the skipper. "The harbor is deeper there."

Jamie groaned again. Burntisland was on the northern side of the Firth, at least six miles away. He gave up all hopes of sleeping that night in his home on the High Street.

"There's the Burntisland lighthouse," announced the captain some time later. "Bear to the starboard side of it, helmsman, and we'll slither up alongside the pier as smooth as thistledown."

"Captain, captain!" screamed Jamie. "I hear breakers!"

"It could not be!" scoffed Robert Clyde. "And yet—I hear 'em too! Hard-a-port, hard-a-port!"

It was too late. The coaster's hull crunched against submerged rocks.

"The de'il take all landsmen!" howled Captain Clyde. "They have moved the lighthouse again, and the pilot

told me not! Still hard-a-port, helmsman; there's no-
where else to turn."

Several more rocks gouged the little vessel before she
got clear of the reef. Now, if ever, was a time to pray for
no contrary wind, for the race was on between filling up
and anchoring down.

Even after he had taken the helm and personally
inched his crippled ship into the intended spot, the
captain still did not order the sails to be lowered.

"We must run her aground again," he explained
gruffly, "or she'll sink yet."

Jamie was the first over the side as the coaster sighed
down into her oozy berth. As he sloshed along by the
pier, Captain Clyde shouted, "Bring anyone you can find,
lad—the maimed, the halt, the blind! We must double-
man the pumps."

There was no sleep for Jamie that night, or for anyone
else of the many who swarmed over the coaster. He
pumped till his arms felt broken. Then he held a candle
for one of the carpenters who hammered emergency
patches onto the hull.

It was two dreary weeks before the ship limped across
to Leith, there to have the bottom newly sheathed all over.

When Jamie had related his tale, Mr. Ireland spoke
up quickly. "Then it's no more of the sea for you, eh,
laddie?"

Jamie was silent. He remembered his vow in the maw

of the hurricane. Furthermore, he knew Father still hoped to see his brightest child follow some higher calling than that of a sailor. And yet . . . and yet . . . there was a sort of freedom about wind and sky and open sea.

"Nay, sire," Jamie heard himself saying. "I think I like it better yet. And Captain Clyde said I gave more aid than the half his crew."

Mr. Ireland walked toward the window. Jamie thought he heard a tone of bitterness in his father's next words. "Then I think you should be off to Greenland, and go a-whaling."

A strange idea scurried across Jamie's mind: *He thinks this will cure me of sea fever.*

With a stubborn tilt of his chin, he answered, "A whaler would suit me grand, after serving my 'prentice-ship on a coaster. Can you arrange to get me on with the fleet?"

Mr. Ireland's shoulders drooped. "We'll see, James. We'll see."

When Jamie next was called into the law office—some days later—he saw his parents and two strangers. One wore the regalia of some high officer on a ship.

"James," began Mr. Ireland, waving first toward the other stranger, "this is another kinsman of mine, Mr. Rowan. And this is Commodore Yan Yonson, of the whaling fleet of Leith."

"Goot morning, young man," said the Commodore.

"How—how do you do," stuttered Jamie.

"Mr. Rowan," continued Jamie's father, "is part owner of the four ships in the fleet, and sees to stocking them with food and paying the sailors. He has been kind enough to bring Commodore Yonson here to talk with us about taking you on his flagship as cabin boy."

The seventeen-year-old's mouth fell open.

"You would like to do dat, eh, young man?" chuckled the Commodore.

"Aye," breathed Jamie. "Aye, that I would."

The officer's eyes twinkled. "And you would like to know why I talk dis way, and why I have sooch a funny name, eh? All boys want to know about dat."

"Mr. Yonson is a Hollander," explained Mr. Rowan. "He got his early experience on Dutch whalers. We were lucky to get him to command our little squadron out of Leith."

"Aye, de *walvisch*—I mean, de whale-fish—and I, we have known each odder a long time," agreed the heavyset Dutchman.

As the conversation went on, Jamie liked his strange new captain more and more. Jolly and gentle at the same time, he seemed already to take a fatherly interest in Jamie's welfare.

At last everything was settled. Commodore Yonson announced the not-too-distant date of sailing, and briefly explained what Jamie would need for the long half-year's voyage.

"He did not list a Bible!" snorted Mother after the visitors had left. "I still wonder whether we should send the lad away to serve so long under a foreigner."

"Silence, lady," soothed her husband. "I daresay the Dutch serve the same God we do. And as for his Bible, Jamie will not leave it behind, list or no list."

(*But reading it like a wee bairn in kirk on the Lord's Day,* thought Jamie—*that's another matter.*)

Bible and boots, jacket and jeans, cap and comforters all went into Jamie's trunk. He whistled "Weel May the Keel Row" as he helped to cart it down to Leith. At last he was really going to sea, on a great three-master of four hundred tons burden!

On a raw day in early spring, the whalers eased out into the Firth of Forth. Past the Isle of May, past St. Andrews Bay, past Bell Rock, past Aberdeen, past Buchan Ness, past the Shetland Islands cruised the stately fleet. Then—Jamie thrilled to see that their course followed the needle of the flagship's deck compass: due north!

And thus it was that Jamie Ireland went fishing for whales. Greenland whales, right whales, bowheads—whatever varied names the sailors might call them by, they were black and ugly and tremendous—sometimes fifty feet long.

From the moment he took his first good look at one spouting its double jet, Jamie knew why it was called a bowhead. The immense lower lip curved upward, for all the world like an archer's bow.

"But why do we call them *right* whales?" he asked a group of friendly sailors one day. "Are there *left* whales too?"

"Nay, nay, laddie! 'Tis because these are the *right* ones to chase. Their blubber boils down to the most oil for lamps and lubricants—and liniments, too. And that ugly bowhead hides the finest black whalebone you ever saw—sometimes twelve feet long."

"Nay, even fifteen feet!" corrected an older seaman.

"And what's the good of whalebone?" inquired the new cabin boy.

"For a whale, it strains out his dinner from the tons of sea he swishes through his mouth. For a gentleman, it might serve as a handle for his knife or whip. And for a lady, it might keep her dry by forming the frame of her umbrella, or—keep her shapely by forming the stays of her corset!"

Jamie kept on learning from the sailors—and from the officers, too. He quickly became a favorite with both groups.

Noticing his nimble step, the crew insisted that he be taught the hornpipe. He could not resist those rollicking rhythms that squeaked out of the little instrument played by a Welsh sailmaker. Soon he was, so all agreed, the finest dancer in the fleet.

Much that Jamie learned from his shipmates caused a drift away from what he had been taught at home, school, and kirk. More and more he spoke the sailors' salty language. And his Bible stayed in the trunk.

No less than three times he sailed out with the whaling fleet in the spring and sailed back to Leith in the fall. Three summers he saw the nights shrink as they neared Spitsbergen, till only snow or clouds kept them from basking in constant sunshine. Three years he watched, his heart thumping, as whaleboats would close in on a harpooned but still deadly monster.

Although his duties did not require it, Jamie even took a few turns in a whaleboat himself. He had to wheedle Commodore Yonson, who had faithfully promised to be responsible for his safety. But the headstrong boy won him over. Gleefully then, along with the others, Jamie risked his neck rowing through breakers, spout-spray, and whale-blood.

Nor were whales the only dangers in the Arctic Sea. Jamie and his shipmates, for pure love of sport, gave chase to any living creature when whales were scarce.

Seals were easy to catch. Walruses (Jamie called them sea-horses) were another matter, and he felt a tusk of one brush too close for comfort.

Great white bears seemed to invite a hunt as they

would lumber across the ice floes. But when a whaleboat came too near, they would dive and surface alongside the gunwales, ready to attack.

A nine-foot narwhal (Jamie called it a unicorn fish) was to be admired for the beauty of its skin, spotted like calico. But it was to be avoided for the peril of the long white horn that jutted out from its forehead.

The ice itself caused dangers. When gales blew toward the dreaded northwest, Jamie would sometimes see as many as seventy ships frozen tight near one another. It might be weeks before the field of ice would crack.

One time Jamie hallooed to six men he saw picking their way across the ice. He soon learned that their ship, though fine and new, had been crushed like a shellfish between two icebergs. Commodore Yonson ordered a flag run up to the foretop as a signal to the rest of the marooned crew. Eventually all of them found safety on the whaler flagship.

But the greatest danger Jamie encountered on any voyage did not stem from whales, walruses, polar bears, or ice. It happened one day as the sequel to a storm.

5
Escape to America

The storm winds slacked to a gentle and favorable breeze. But a storm in Arctic regions often seemed to leave the ocean uneasy in its hidden depths. No whitecaps broke the surface, but the whole sea rolled as if some waterlogged giant were shaking his shoulders. This was the much-feared "lofty swell" that plagues all Greenland sailors. It left Commodore Yonson's flagship wallowing helplessly, unable to ride the breeze and continue on course.

During the gale all canvas had been furled. The smaller crosspieces on the masts, such as the topgallant yard high on the mainmast, had also been slung to larger and lower spars, the better to weather the blow.

If the whaler were ever to get over being becalmed, all sails must be trimmed. That was why Jamie Ireland heard the bosun shout, "A volunteer, my lads, a volunteer! Which of you will venture up to the topgallant masthead and rig the topgallant block?"

Quick as a heedless cat dashing before the hoofs of a team, Jamie sprang forward. Up the mainmast he scampered, using the rope ladder made by ratlines on the shrouds.

When he passed the first doubling of the masts and started to climb the main topmast, he began to realize why no one had disputed his privilege. The swell gave a constantly changing but only moderate slant to the deck. But the higher he got in the ship's rigging, the wider he found himself being swung from side to side.

When he reached the crosstrees, where the main topmast joined the main topgallant mast, he was being whipped through the air in what seemed a full quarter-circle, and that at dizzying speed. To make matters worse, he looked up and saw that only the bare double ropes of the shrouds, with no ratlines crossed, formed the next part of his upward route.

Gritting his teeth, he unfastened the pulley block, gripped it in his left hand, and began to shinny up the ropes with one hoisting arm and two backstopping legs. Arriving at last at the topgallant masthead, he untied the rope there in order to pass it through the block.

At that instant the block slipped from his white-knuckled fingers. He grabbed for it in vain. At the same

His whole body swung giddily over the sea.

time, his legs became untwisted from the shrouds.

By one hand he clutched the rope. His whole body swung giddily—now over the deck, now over open sea, now bounced against the mast, now spinning out over the sea again on the other side.

Sky, sea, and ship blurred before Jamie's eyes. All that mattered now was that rope, and his good right hand.

Finally snagging another rope with one foot, he curled his body into the relative safety of the shrouds. As he clung there, dazed, he became aware of a strange stillness on the deck below.

Then he realized why. His shipmates, to a man, were watching to see the outcome. Not a voice was raised, not a toe was tapped, lest the sound distract him from the job he had to do.

Inch by inch he worked his way back down to the crosstrees and grabbed the slippery block, still dangling there. Inch by inch he crept back up to the masthead, ran the rope through the block, and fastened it to the iron ring below. Ratline by ratline he eased his way back down the main topmast, down the mainmast, down to the blessed flat planks of the quarterdeck.

"Bravo!"

"Bully!"

"Great work, lad!"

As sailors and officers alike pounded him on the back, Jamie suddenly began to tremble. He looked aloft where he had just been swinging, and he shook still more.

"Quick! A pannikin of rum, afore he faints!"

Jamie gulped the fiery liquor as eager hands held the cup to his lips. Soon the shock passed over, but Jamie never forgot. Sometimes he would jerk up in bed, his nightshirt drenched with sweat, having dreamed that he swung once more from the main topgallant mast of the whaler.

Autumn—and journey's end—came, as it always does. The tanned, keen-eyed nineteen-year-old who strode down the gangplank into Leith and eagerly scooped his pay into his pocket had grown little in size since he was boxing champion of the Latin School. But in strength, in speed, in freedom from restraint, and in ways of the world, he fancied he had become something more of a man. Proudly he plunked down silver to buy rum for himself and several messmates.

When he stumbled out the door of the grogshop in Leith, Jamie still had enough wit to realize he must not go home in such a state. *As well go home tomorrow,* he reflected. *I'll have no trouble finding a berth for tonight.*

Walking by the wharves with more than his customary care, he passed a packet ship. The crew bustled about as if almost ready to depart.

"Ahoy, matey!" piped Jamie. "When do ye sail?"

"We're off for Baltimore on the midnight tide," came the answer.

Jamie now lurched toward the section of Leith where lodgers could find rooms. He squalled out the shadier stanzas of one of the many sea chanties he had learned.

"Well, now, would you but look! No fool like a drunken sailor, so they say."

The voice had a familiar ring. Jamie turned to see Hastings and several cronies strolling toward him. All of them were dressed like the young dandies of Edinburgh which they now had become.

"Ahoy, Hastings!" Jamie returned his greeting. "Age has improved neither your looks, your manners, nor your wit, I'm sorry to see."

"Hoot! You're the one to talk about wit, that staggers like a milk-sick cow."

Jamie frowned. "Stand aside," he warned, "and guard your tongue. I would not like to have to whip you again."

"Aha, Hastings," teased one of the other dandies. "Be sure your sins will find you out. You told us the only one who ever beat you was a great, braw bruiser."

Hastings flushed. "Will you pay more heed to the words of a seafaring sot than to mine?"

"Aye, lads," boasted Jamie, growing bolder. "I had your bonny hero begging for mercy. Why, I'll fight him and two others of you now, if you will but stretch a rope between us."

Even Hastings joined in the laughter. "What a braggart!" he whooped. "Why, you could scarce fight Donald and Murray, here."

Jamie flung off his jacket and advanced swinging toward the two slightly built young men that Hastings had indicated. One of them threw up his arms in self-defense, then wrung his hand and squealed in agony.

"De'il take you, you have thrown my thumb out of joint!" he whined.

"We make no claim to be fighters," protested the other young man. "But Hastings, now—surely ye cannot conquer the mighty Hastings."

Jamie's senses were too much dulled to realize how slily these backscratching dandies were prodding their master into an unnecessary fight. Jamie walked into the trap.

"Put up your fists, Hastings," he challenged. "Or have you forgot everything you learned in school?"

Hastings shot a dark look at Donald, Murray, and the rest. Slowly he assumed his boxing stance.

Jamie began to dance and bob and weave, as before. Fighting without caution, he landed more and harder blows in the first few seconds than he had sometimes achieved in an entire fight.

Suddenly he found himself sprawling in the dust. As he clutched his jaw and stifled a groan, his opponent still towered over him.

"Had you forgot there is no schoolmaster to care

whether we hit above the breath?" mocked Hastings.

That clip on the chin was a lucky one for Jamie. As he picked himself up, stalling for precious seconds, his addled head began to clear. He realized that Hastings would not stop now until he had battered into helplessness the one person who had ever succeeded in puncturing his bluffs. Jamie also remembered his father's self-test and realized that he had entangled himself in a battle when it was not "a time to fight."

No chance to think more of that now; Hastings' fists struck Jamie from all angles like a rain of sledgehammers.

One eye had swollen shut and blood dripped from Jamie's nose and mouth before the last of his fogginess had been knocked out of him. Pain sharpened his reflexes and he started boxing like the Jamie of old.

Now Hastings began to feel the force of muscles hardened by tugging halyards in a storm, of hands made horny by pulling an oar in a whaleboat. His face, too, soon showed the marks of well-aimed fists.

The fight had begun with Jamie losing. It continued on even terms. It ended as a slaughter. Hastings' angry tears mingled with blood, dust, and sweat as he gamely picked himself up again and again.

At last Jamie crunched both fists in quick succession against Hastings' jaws. The tall youth crumpled like a stoved-in skiff.

"Fetch a physician!" cried Donald. "He's hurt!"

"He struck his head on that rock as he fell," added Murray.

"Look at that blood—"

His friends huddled around their leader's limp form. Then one of them looked up and shook his fist at Jamie.

"Think not that you can carry this off, ye sotted swine!" he screamed. "Nobody kills Lord Huntingdon's son without penalty!"

Jamie's face went white beneath its mask of blood. He remembered now that Hastings was the family name of Lord Huntingdon.

Feeling drained of strength, either of body or of mind, he slunk away, leaving Hastings' courtiers to care for him.

That great hulk will not really die, he told himself. *But what if his father hales me into court for assault?*

Although the night was cool, he broke into a fresh sweat to realize that every witness of the fight would doubtless swear to whatever Hastings said. *Even Father's skill could scarce keep me out of gaol in such a case.* He shivered at the thought of his old fear—iron bars, locked doors.

Jamie thrust his skinned and aching hands into his jingling pockets. Then—suddenly—he seemed to feel a way out of his predicament, a way to keep his precious freedom.

He quickened his pace, glancing up at the stars to see how near it was to midnight. He thought hard, trying to remember at which wharf he had seen the packet ship anchored.

And thus it happened that Jamie Ireland left behind his home, his family, his native land, and came to the colonies of America.

6

Schoolmaster in the Settlements

Jamie Ireland urged his weary horse along the path that wound downhill from the mountains of northern Virginia. He smiled to glimpse again through leafless branches his place of lodging—a small log cabin like all the others in the little settlement on the Shenandoah River. To this backwoods spot he had found his way after landing at Baltimore, eighty miles east in the colony of Maryland.

"Jemmy, Jemmy!" cried little Samantha, youngest child of the family with whom he boarded. (Jamie was quickly getting used to the American form of his nickname.)

"Jemmy, there was a man here yesterday to see you," announced the little girl, swinging along with her hand in his stirrup, her toes kicking the fallen leaves.

"To see me!" gasped Jamie. "What about?"

53

"Oh, I don't know," prattled the child. "I think he wants you for a schoolmaster. You wouldn't be a schoolmaster, would you, Jemmy?"

"Not I, lass." He chuckled in relief. "But was there some other errand, sure enough?"

She shook her yellow braids. "You'll have to ask my ma."

Jamie dismounted and led his horse to the log stable. Joining the family for supper, he learned that a stranger had indeed come looking for a schoolteacher. The settlers, impressed by their lodger's intelligence, had recommended him.

"Where's the home of this man?" inquired Jamie, between rapid bites of the cornbread he had quickly come to like.

"In a settlement called Cross Roads," replied Samantha's father, "some thirty-five or forty miles from here, near the North Fork of the Shenandoah."

"He was a fine gentleman, Jemmy," added the mother. "I reckon you'd better go see what it's like at Cross Roads."

With this scant amount of information, Jamie resaddled his horse next day and rode off upriver. The profits from his last whaling voyage, though increased by a few odd jobs, would not last too much longer. He was ready to look for steadier work—even if it meant teaching school!

Jamie sucked in his cheeks when he learned that the "fine gentleman" who had so impressed the frontier family was nothing of the sort. Cross Roads did need a schoolteacher, though; that much of the story had been true. Jamie found the nearest person to a "fine gentleman" in the tiny village, and frankly asked him for the job.

"Well, young man," replied the middle-aged farmer, "let me holler for a few of my neighbors."

Soon five backwoodsmen gathered around a fire blazing on the kitchen hearth.

"Stranger, can you read?" asked one.

Jamie nodded, not trusting himself to speak lest a laugh slip out.

"Fetch him your Bible, Nathan, and let him spell out a few verses."

Jamie felt a twinge of homesickness as he read the familiar sentences—even though he now thought them rather childish.

"Can you cipher?" inquired another patron of education.

"Aye."

"Do you know the rule of three?"

Jamie proceeded to demonstrate that he did by working a simple problem.

"Can you write a fair hand?"

His eyes twinkling, Jamie wrote, "James Ireland, late

Jamie felt a twinge of homesickness
as he read the familiar sentences.

of Edinburgh but now a resident of Virginia, can write well enough to become schoolmaster at Cross Roads."

Two of his questioners could read well enough to blink and then cackle at his little joke.

"Young man, you're hired! Can you commence on Monday next? We've already lost enough time on the children's book learning since the last schoolmaster left us." Nathan Fincastle, from whose Bible Jamie had read, spoke for the group.

Jamie hurried back downriver, packed his few belongings, said his good-bys (including a kiss for little Samantha), and moved. He almost felt he was dreaming when he found himself in a schoolroom again—as the *teacher*.

School at Cross Roads was a far cry from Latin School at Edinburgh. In the first place, his pupils included a few girls along with the boys. Jamie had all ages from five to fifteen in one room. The older pupils had to help with the farm work, and so were often absent from school for weeks at a time.

Somewhat to his surprise, Jamie did not find it hard to maintain order. His firm but merry way quickly won all but the meanest. His heavy hand with a hickory rod kept the rest in check.

Jamie knew all too well how little he knew on many subjects. But he knew so much more than any of his pupils, or their parents even, that he quickly had the reputation of being an able teacher. He was invited into many homes and soon made the acquaintance of everyone in the community. His broad Scots accent and lively spirit made him popular.

Many of Jamie's invitations were to parties and dances on "the Lord's Day," as he still called it. Although he had drifted away from any real interest in church, Jamie had still tried to respect the special day of worship. In Cross Roads almost no one else did so. A few Quakers held their solemn, silent meetings. Jamie's friend Nathan Fincastle attended occasional New Light services. These were almost the only exceptions. Everyone else considered Sunday to be a day for gaiety.

Of course Jamie was invited whenever one of the farmers had a husking bee. He was not slow, either, to take advantage of the usual custom when one of his older girl pupils would shell out a red ear of corn. The teen-ager's cheeks would turn as rosy as the kernels when the handsome young schoolteacher would plant a kiss there.

It was at a husking bee one autumn evening that Jamie heard a question which started him toward his greatest adventure.

During much of the time that evening, he happened to be shucking corn beside Nathan Fincastle.

"I've heard naught but good about your teaching," he complimented Jamie.

"Thankee! You folk are most kind."

The older man smiled. "You must have had a gentle

rearing. I daresay you always went to church then."

"Oh, aye," replied Jamie, "And took the prize at kirk every half-year when the minister would examine us on the Bible and the catechism."

"Catechism! Now, that's interesting. Tell me, what did the catechism teach you about . . . umm . . . say . . . faith in Christ?"

Jamie leaned back against a log upright in the crude frontier barn. "Let me see, was that question 85 or question 86? 'Twas 86; I'm sure of it." He cleared his throat, then spoke in rapid singsong tones. " 'Faith in Jesus Christ is a saving grace, whereby we receive and rest upon him alone for salvation, as he is offered to us in the gospel.' "

Nathan Fincastle nodded, pleased. "You know the words well, and that is good. But do you know *him*—the One of whom the words speak?"

Jamie looked down at the puncheon floor, then glanced up again. "I'm not sure I—"

"A man finds faith in God through his heart, not his head, young man. Finding faith means finding Jesus Christ and giving your whole self to him."

As the gray-haired man talked on, Jamie could find nothing to resent either in his words or in his manner. Yet he felt uncomfortable. *It must be because I want to do some sort of mischief,* Jamie decided, *and this old man is so good I would not want to do it in his presence.*

Soon enough he realized just what "mischief" he wanted to do. One man who had drunk too much hard cider had been making mocking remarks about the guests all evening. Seeing Jamie and Mr. Fincastle in conversation, he asked in a too-loud whisper: "Now, who'll lay me a wager what's to come of that session? Will the schoolmaster make a scholar out of the old man—or will the old man make a convert out of the schoolmaster?"

Slipping away from his companion, Jamie whispered to some of his older schoolboys: "Will ye stand in a line betwixt me and Mr. Fincastle so he will not see what I am about?"

The boys, only too glad to share in the excitement, made themselves into a screen between Jamie and Fincastle. Dropping to his knees, Jamie tackled the troublemaker. With hard words and harder blows, he taught an out-of-school lesson.

Waiting till he was breathing normally, Jamie rejoined Nathan Fincastle as if nothing had happened. He suspected that his friend had heard the two arguing voices and knew well enough what had gone on, but it was never mentioned. Without Jamie quite realizing how, the conversation turned again to religion.

He next saw Mr. Fincastle on a Sunday some months later, as he was beginning an important trip. He had heard that a newcomer had moved onto Smith's Creek, a mile to the east. This new settler hailed from none other place than Edinburgh.

Jamie doubted that he would ever again walk the High Street—except in his dreams, when he did so frequently. He had not tried to write his family, fearing he might bring shame upon them and trouble upon himself. But a possibility, however slim, of getting some news about them—this caused him to urge young Thomas Buck, Jr., to ride with him to Smith's Creek.

When they met Nathan Fincastle on the way, he warmly shook Jamie's hand. "How are you, my fine young friend?"

"Very well, thankee," returned Jamie. During the small talk, he groped into his pockets and shared some fine peaches he had just picked.

There 'tis again, something seemed to say inside him— *that same strange feeling you had at the husking bee. You must be planning some wrong deed, and it makes you uncomfortable to be within the sight of this godly old man.*

Jamie tossed his head. "Hey, laddie," he called to his riding companion, "shall we wager five shillings and race our horses a quartermile this fine summer morning?"

"Done!" agreed Tom Buck.

Mr. Fincastle's smile faded, but he said nothing except a pleasant good-by. The two horses galloped away on the eastward trail.

To Jamie's joy he discovered that the newcomer on Smith's Creek did indeed know the Irelands and could bring a good report only a few weeks old. Through Mr. McRae (for that was his name) Jamie had hopes of renewing at least some contact with his family. He visited on Smith's Creek often in the months that followed.

Not only Mr. McRae but also the community in which he lived impressed Jamie favorably. There seemed to be many young people who, like himself, had just turned twenty. Dances were even more frequent than in Cross Roads. The colonists cheered wildly to see Jamie dance a hornpipe on the top of a tiny table. When he leaped down from his perch, he also set the pace in jigs, minuets, and anything else the fiddler could play.

Finding that Smith's Creek also needed a school-teacher, Jamie soon heard tempting invitations.

"Jemmy, you'd make the best schoolmaster we've ever had."

"Come over, boy; we'll make it worth your trouble."

"We'd get value received from our tuition just to see that little Scot dance on a table!"

Younger friends, jollier times, and higher pay made up Jamie's mind. In the fall he moved to Smith's Creek—as schoolmaster and life of the party.

He would never have believed it if anyone had told him then what his occupation in Smith's Creek would be just one school year later.

7
Haunted by His Own Words

"Have you heard the latest scandal?" Mr. McRae asked Jamie one day. "Five of these hedge preachers among the Separates have gotten themselves jailed down in Spotsylvania County."

"Serves them right!" said Harry Routon, another friend.

"And who are these Separates?" inquired Jamie.

"Why, man, they're radicals!" pronounced McRae. "I think little of any church myself. Yet, if a man will go, let him go to the Established Church, as is proper and right. But these backwoods bishops cry out their strange doctrines and hold illegal meetings. As (I'm told) the prosecutor said at their trial in Spotsylvania, 'These preachers can't even meet a man on the road without trying to ram a text of Scripture down his throat!'"

"They're the same as the New Lights, aren't they?" asked Harry Routon.

"Aye, and de'il take the whole rabble-rousing mob of 'em!"

Jamie blinked. He found little likeness between these reports and the conduct of his New Light friend Nathan Fincastle.

Out of curiosity, then, he accepted McRae's invitation to become a "spy." Together they visited one session of a special yearly meeting of the Separates in that area.

Silently they mingled with farm families clothed in homespun. Silently they heard sermons from ministers who seemed to feel each word as well as speak it. Silently they observed warm greetings of friends afterward.

"Well, my young countryman," began McRae as they rode home, "what think you of them?"

Jamie evaded the question. "You're the elder; what think *you?*"

McRae snorted. "Any bairn who had learnt his *ABC* could make a better shift at preaching. Why can they not go to the Established Church, where the parsons at least have some degree of education and common sense?"

"And they make such a show of calling one another 'Brother,'" added Jamie. "Yet, I see no cause for casting them into prison."

The older man's face became more serious. "It will not do for folk of consequence to start following such disturbers of the peace." Solemnly taking Jamie by the hand, he continued, *"Brother,* you and I—we'll stick to our own ways—aye?"

In spite of Jamie's nagging doubts these days that there really was a God, he joined McRae then in a sacred vow. By Father, Son, and Holy Ghost they swore that they would never become Separates.

Another new interest now took Jamie's fancy.

"Come to my singing school this week-end, Jemmy!"

The invitation came from Thomas Buck, Jr., in whose home Jamie had spent many lively hours.

"Tom, you've gotten to be as much a schoolmaster as I," exclaimed Jamie. "Do ye have singing classes in several places?"

"I do indeed," replied Tom, "but the best one is at Colonel Pugh's, where I'm due this weekend. And I have a special reason for wanting your company."

Jamie dropped his voice. "Will you not tell me what it is?"

Tom beamed. "I think a lot of you, boy. I'd like to see you married to a proper girl—one as nice as the wife I met and wooed over in Maryland. Fully a quarter of my pupils at Colonel Pugh's are females, and one especially —well, well, it's hard to describe her."

But Tom tried. So rich were the adjectives he used that Jamie soon consented to make the twenty-two mile trip with him.

During an intermission between tunes, Jamie introduced himself to Permelia, Colonel Pugh's black-haired daughter.

"Mr. Buck must bring you back again, Mr. Ireland," she said. "How sweetly you sang just now!"

Jamie smiled and leaned closer. " 'Tis you, my lass, who deserve that compliment. I noticed your voice, too. It soars like a nightingale's."

"Oh, Mr. Ireland!" She fanned her cheeks, even though they showed no hint of a blush.

Seeing how eagerly she swallowed the flattery, Jamie searched for more extravagant compliments. "Your tresses are like—whistling blackbirds—" He was proud of that one.

Permelia batted her lashes. "Would you turn a poor country girl's head with your pretty talk?" she asked.

Jamie enjoyed such bantering off and on for two days, without any deeper impression being made. Yet he did not forget the girl's dark locks, or her dimpled smile, or the delicacy of her movements when she danced. He also remembered Tom's pronouncements about the wealth of Permelia's family, and their obvious willingness to see her married.

Still another pursuit that took the young schoolmaster's hours was the composition of poetry. Jamie had always had a way with words. Now he wrestled with rhymes and meters to write songs and verses—most of them

"Would you turn a poor country girl's head, Mr. Ireland?"

rather clever, so Jamie thought. He bought and read books that his father would never have allowed inside the house, the better to frame his own jests.

One springtime morning Jamie strolled toward his schoolhouse, knowing he had several minutes to spare. To his genuine pleasure he chanced to meet his old friend Nathan Fincastle.

After the usual greetings Mr. Fincastle remarked, "I think, my dear young friend, that I have seen some of your poetical compositions."

"Well! And how do ye like them?"

The gray-haired man smiled. "Oh, they do well enough for the occasions they were applied to. But now, I'd like to speak my mind freely, if you won't get offended."

Jamie shook his head in lordly tolerance. "Nothing you would say could give me offense."

"Well, then," he proceeded, "I believe that all gifts, like all grace, come from God. You possess great gifts, though you possess not the grace of God. Even so, it seems but reasonable that where God has bestowed a gift, it should be improved for him, and not in the service of the devil."

Jamie nodded, unable to find fault with Nathan Fincastle's quaint logic.

"If, therefore," continued the older man, "you would compose a poem for *me,* I would give you a subject."

"Fair enough," agreed Jamie, smiling at his friend. "The subject, then, is *charity*."

Charity . . . charity . . . surely he means more than mere giving of alms, mused Jamie. But he stubbornly decided against showing his ignorance by inquiring what the word really meant.

Mr. Fincastle explained without the asking. As they parted he called, "My friend, the next time I see you, I'll expect also to see your piece on charity, or brotherly love."

Brotherly love—so that's it. Jamie recalled the loving way that Separates named one another "Brother," even when they were no kin.

He hurried on to school. That afternoon he began work on Nathan Fincastle's poem. True brotherly love, so Jamie had learned in his childhood, must grow out of God's love. Now he made this the theme of his poem.

By Thursday evening it was completed—all eleven stanzas of it. Jamie wrote in the usual flowery style of the 1760's. One stanza he especially liked. It ended with these words:

". . . When the great God pronounces forth
    Eternal peace to us on earth,
    If we by faith believe the word
    Of Jesus Christ his Son, our Lord."

Somehow these lines kept jingling through his head. Even lessons in school on Friday could not drive them out. That afternoon he happened to walk with Tom Buck, and they sang "Barbara Allen"; yet Jamie still heard the words of his own poem. He wondered why.

"Don't forget the barn-raising at Fincastle's tomorrow," Tom reminded him as they parted.

The floor of the new barn already lay in place when Jamie arrived on Saturday morning.

Mr. Fincastle bustled out to meet him. "Have you written the poem?"

Jamie silently handed him the verses.

He read them through, his expression growing more delighted with every line.

"Wonderful! Wonderful!" he exulted. "Oh, we must sing them for the people, since you were so wise as to write them in a hymn meter."

Scrambling up to the new-laid floor, he flung his arms and shouted, "Come! Come, good people, and gather round!"

In lower tones he begged Jamie to help him sing. Reluctantly Jamie mounted the rude stage and agreed with Mr. Fincastle on which familiar hymn tune they should try.

Swinging his left hand around Jamie's waist, the happy old farmer held the poem in the other, and tapped the time with his foot. Thus they sang as a duet the words that Jamie had written.

After the new barn stood stark and tall against the

budding hills, Jamie joined his host in the house. He flopped into a chair. In an offhand manner he called Mr. Fincastle's attention to the stanza that had kept on ringing in his ears for a day and a half. "Can you assign any reason why it is so?"

The old man tried to hide a smile by looking down.

Jamie flushed. *He must think me a fool for asking such a question.*

Leaving the house, he determined to try harder than ever to rid himself of his poem and the questions it raised in his mind. As soon as he was out of earshot, he made the forest paths echo with some of his wildest ditties.

Still the words started again:

"When the great God pronounces forth
    Eternal peace to us on earth . . ."

He stopped and bent over, hands on knees, and shook his head like a spaniel flinging water out of its ears.

The words crept back:

". . . If we by faith believe the word
    Of Jesus Christ his Son, our Lord."

Jamie was scheduled to attend a dance that Saturday night. He went, and cavorted over the dance floor. Yet, the hymn stanza still thumped inside his head—louder than the fiddler's tunes.

Sunday morning came. On an impulse he walked to a home where he had heard that a few Separates—no preacher among them—held simple services. They sang hymns, some of which Jamie remembered from long-ago days in an Edinburgh kirk. They read several Bible passages as if each were a letter from a well-known friend. They told of ways that God had showed them his goodness. They prayed. They discussed religious questions.

Jamie's quick wits made the usual quick impression during this last activity. "Like the man in the Bible," complimented one young Separate in parting, "you have the five talents."

Jamie had planned to eat dinner and spend the afternoon with the Jackmon family, who lived about a mile away. Old Mrs. Jackmon, a devout Presbyterian, had attended the same morning service he had.

As he walked alone toward his friends' home, the lines of his own poem still chimed in his brain.

Suddenly he stopped. *Eternal peace on earth? Why did I write such words? I have no peace! I know no faith, no love, no Lord, no God. How can I ever expect to find peace—on earth or in heaven either?*

8

The Beginning of the Greatest Adventure

Jamie gobbled the Jackmons' Virginia ham and buttery cornbread with more than his usual speed and less than his usual merry talk. Repeatedly he found himself losing the thread of conversation. As soon as possible he excused himself and hurried outside.

Finding a shelf of rock in the shadow of Massanutten Mountain, he sat down.

For the first time in his life, he prayed—not just repeated a prayer someone had taught him, but really prayed.

"God?" he whispered. It was a question—a question born of doubting, of trying to push back uncomfortable thoughts. "Is it thy presence I feel, O God?"

He paused.

"What is it, God?" he asked again. "What troubles my mind like a storm at sea? What must I do?"

He thought of the wrongs he had done. The idle words, the thoughtless deeds, the wasted hours and years, the disappointment he had brought to well-meaning parents—yes, even the brutal beating he had given Hastings, who had intended the same for him—all of these now crowded into his mind.

Something greater loomed up behind these thoughts and seemed to overcloud them all. *'Tis more than the wrongs I have done; 'tis the fact that I am wrong myself!* He furrowed his forehead as he realized that he had lived full twenty years without seeking the good of any living soul save Jamie Ireland.

Boys on the High Street with only tattered jackets between their backs and Scottish winters . . . hungry beggars on the road to Leith . . . sailors whose homesick spirits cried for someone who cared—all of these Jamie Ireland had seen. Yet he had scarcely given a serious thought to finding the needs of his fellowmen—or to finding God, if God there be.

"God, forgive me!" His knuckles dug in against his eyelids. "And show me what I must do."

Shadows of tall oaks stretched long before him as he arose and trudged back toward the house. At the turning of the path, he met Mrs. Jackmon. Each seemed to guess that the other had also been praying. Jamie opened his mouth twice to speak but said nothing in his embarrassment.

The old woman gave him a look of understanding. "May every one of us be praying for ourselves," she murmured, "and may God be for us all!"

During the next few days the confusion in Jamie's mind grew worse. His pupils gaped at his blank looks and sudden bursts of temper.

Sometimes he would say to himself, *I'll reform my ways and so find grace in God's sight.* Then again he would realize, *'Tis no use; God wants more of me than mere keeping of rules.*

He reflected over the many grapples with death his brief life had already brought—that storm on board the coaster, icebergs grinding against the side of Commodore Yonson's flagship, the wallowing agonies of dying bowhead whales, that wild pendulum-ride from the main topgallant mast. The realization thudded home like a well-aimed harpoon: *God must have some grand purpose in mind; why else would he have spared a lad so heedless?*

Walking through the woods after school one day, Jamie somehow found himself repeating a sentence that sounded strangely familiar: "I am found of them that sought me not."

Is that Scripture? he wondered.

Hurrying home, he pulled out the Bible that his mother had once lovingly packed for him. Searching Old Testament and New, he at last ran across the words in the book of Isaiah—chapter 65, verse 1: "I am sought of them that asked not for me; I am found of them that sought me not."

'Tis true! cried Jamie's conscience. *God himself spoke that verse. As for me, I thought to find Fincastle's favor, not God's, in writing my poem about brotherly love. Yet, 'tis God himself I am beginning to find.*

But how to find what God wanted him to do? How to find peace and freedom and salvation in God? These were the questions that filled Jamie's waking hours and plagued his nights.

His companions soon saw or heard that Jamie was "acting strange." They tried in every possible way to tease him back into the gay, devil-may-care hornpipe-dancer they had known. So constantly did they torment him that Jamie had a bed moved into a corner of his schoolhouse, and slipped off to sleep there many an evening rather than face their mocking.

Tom Buck rode up to the schoolhouse one afternoon as the pupils were leaving.

"Jemmy, have you room for another scholar?" he asked. "There's one coming to board at our house, in order to go to your school."

Jamie frowned, his suspicions aroused. "And who is this person?"

"Permelia Pugh; she wants the benefit of your tutoring for the next three months."

Long after Tom had gone, Jamie still felt as if he had company, for he wrestled with attractive and tempting thoughts. Earlier he had resisted the idea of losing some of his freedom in marriage. Now marriage seemed a way to rid himself of his worries. Permelia was gay and lighthearted. Married to her, Jamie would have no time and little heart to concern himself with matters more serious than sociables, dances, and corn-huskings. And the black-haired girl would be like a ripe apple for his picking, no doubt about that.

Marry her! Jamie told himself. *Marry her, get her father's gold, and forget this foolishness. Who's to say you nay?*

As he stalked home through darkening woods, Jamie knew he was leaving at least one temptation behind him. *No pretty face or form shall throw me off my course,* he vowed.

Soon he was warned of the approach of another struggle. Harry Routon passed by while Jamie's pupils were enjoying their noon recess.

"McRae has just now heard about you," reported Harry. "He was away on a trip, you know. And when we told him how you are acting, you should have heard the old boy swear!"

Jamie mustered a faint smile. "Is that all he said?"

Harry Routon shook his head. "He vowed he'd lose no time in telling you what he thought of such behavior. So you'd better give up your religion now, Jemmy. McRae is probably on his way."

Jamie's schoolroom was empty late that afternoon when he heard hoofbeats.

"James Ireland!"

Jamie jerked upright. The stern voice in a Scots accent made him feel for an instant that he had again been demoted to a pupil, and that he was being called upon to give an account of his conduct.

"James Ireland!" shouted McRae again. "If you are in there, I command you to come out."

Let me say the right words, Lord, asked Jamie as he stepped to the door.

"In the name of heaven," trumpeted McRae, "what's the matter with you?"

He did not wait for an answer. As he alighted from his horse, he continued to speak in an angry staccato. "I hear you're going to be mighty good now. I hear you think you're about to get yourself converted. Converted!"

He repeated the word as if it were an insult. "Converted! Let me tell you something, my fickle young friend, *I'm* here to convert you. There's another dance on Monday next. I'll convert you to lead the ball that night, and to turn away from all these foolish notions. And— what's more—remember our oath, Jamie, remember our oath!"

Jamie still had offered no word of reply. His look was

solemn, straightforward, unafraid. "I know you come as my friend," he began at length. "But do you truly think that a dance or an oath or anything else of human invention is more important to a man than the way he stands before God?"

McRae started to spout another angry remark, then changed his mind in the presence of Jamie's unflinching gaze.

The dialogue continued—on a different level.

When McRae stepped up into his stirrups several minutes later, Jamie had a thought that surprised him. *McRae is not far from finding the Lord. He may be closer already than I am.*

After an especially dismal Friday night in his schoolhouse, Jamie turned again to his Bible at dawn one Saturday. A New Testament verse gave him new insight: "Believe on the Lord Jesus Christ."

Believe—aye, that's it. And acknowledge that he is Lord and Master over all.

Gradually he began to realize that he must drop all trust in his own efforts and turn himself over to Jesus Christ. But how? How?

So many of Jamie's friends had found his schoolhouse hideout now that he moved in with the Jackmons. He had resigned his schoolteaching job anyway. He could no longer concentrate on his work, and decided it was dishonest to take any more tuition money.

Each morning he would climb a little way up Massanutten Mountain, Bible and hymnbook in hand. There he would read, pray, and think. Out of one such session came a new poem—an earnest prayer to God.

Tom Buck found his new retreat. "How is the state of your mind now?" he inquired.

"The same as it was when last you saw me," replied Jamie, "when you hid beside the road for fear I would preach at you as we met."

"Jemmy, Jemmy!" Tom shook his head. "I'd rather lose five hundred pounds than lose your conversation and company. You were the idol of us all. Why did you—"

"Aye, that's it," interrupted Jamie. "I was an idol, a god of my own making. Therein lies the trouble."

Tom frowned. "Don't be a fool, Jemmy. All I meant to say was that your sprightly behavior made you such a favorite. Now you've changed. Why? Why must you try to be different from the rest of us?"

Why indeed? Jamie looked down, remembering his merry times with Tom Buck and Mrs. Buck and Harry Routon and all the rest. Why should he be different from the crowd?

"I'm not sure why, Tom," he muttered, "but I believe I'm close to finding it out."

Tom raised his eyebrows. "Can it be true, then—what some have said? Are you really losing your senses? Why, if I would be your true friend, I should go to that blacksmith down the road and order a nice handsome chain to keep you from destroying yourself!"

Jamie pulled a sheet of paper out of his Bible. "So you think me a fool. Can fools write such poetry as this? Read the folly I have written here."

Silently Tom read through Jamie's prayer poem. He read it a second time. He paced a short distance, glancing down again at the paper as he walked.

Finally he returned the sheet. "Maybe we're all fools, Jemmy," he mumbled. "Maybe you're the only wise man amongst us."

Jamie's hopes were renewed by Tom Buck's signs of interest. Still he tussled with his own doubts. Even when John Pickett, a Separate minister from Fauquier County, came to preach on Smith's Creek one summer day, Jamie could not feel sure that he had found God, or God's way for his life.

"I will not take a truth on trust from any man," he explained. "I must have some further evidence from God."

Mr. Pickett gave Jamie an elder-brotherly smile and a word of encouragement. After holding services two days, he returned over Massanutten Mountain to preach at White House. "I'll come back soon," he promised.

McRae and Tom Buck rode across the mountain to hear the preacher again. Jamie noticed that the two friends lost no opportunity these days to attend a preaching service—to learn more about the new ideas that had begun to snare their minds.

On this night they stopped by to report to Jamie on the service at White House. Shortly after ten o'clock Jamie walked with them down the creek bottom between fields of rustling corn.

"Pray with me before we part," he asked.

Each man in turn prayed. While McRae spoke audibly to God, Jamie somehow found himself speaking inwardly.

He never knew how or why the picture flashed into his mind. But suddenly he was reliving that long-ago experience on the whaler after the storm. He went through each terrifying moment of it—the climb up the slippery rope, the loss of the pulley block, the dizzying swing out over the sea. One sentence beat in his mind. *The rigging held.*

Yes, the rigging had held. He would not have been able to climb the mast at all, had the rigging failed. And even when his fumbling had almost caused him to fall, even when his one link with safety had been that single rope, the rigging had held.

Faith in God is like that! Jamie silently shouted. *No chance to save myself; if the rigging had broken, it would have meant certain death. But even when the swell was stoutest and my grip was weak, the rigging held.*

Jamie straightened up. He had his answer. Later he

described the experience, "My whole soul ran out by faith on God"—as his whole body had run out by nimble feet on many a yardarm.

For a long time he walked in the fields after his two friends had said good night and gone. " 'Tis all from thee, O God," he confessed. "I can do nothing but trust myself to thy grace and mercy. I yield me to thy Son Jesus Christ. Only in him is peace, and freedom, and everything that truly makes a man."

And from that nighttime instant down through all the nights and days that followed, Jamie Ireland was Jesus Christ's man—strong body, quick mind, stout soul.

9
Dreams and Debates

No longer did Jamie Ireland spend his days moping in the schoolhouse or walking alone in the woods. Now he felt a surge of that same vigor that had driven him to become a champion boxer, a reckless seaman, a spur-of-the-moment runaway to America.

For the first time in his twenty-one years, however, all his energies were channeled. Now he tried to make every waking thought and act count for God.

Even when he was asleep his subconscious mind took note of the experience that had changed his life. Jamie had always been a great dreamer, but never before had he known such a dream as this. . . .

A man riding a red horse took him prisoner and carried him over two high mountains. As they worked their way down the ridges of the second, a small settlement came into view. To the right were several buildings; to the left, an open field with one little old house. It had only one window; as they drew nearer, Jamie saw that there were bars across it. The man took him inside, then left and locked the door. There Jamie stayed alone, a prisoner, until by prayer the door swung open.

Then he journeyed again—down beautiful walks, up gentle slopes, through rocky and cold valleys, sometimes in water and sometimes on land, until at last he came to a gorgeous and lofty building called "My Father's House."

Jamie awoke. The dream lingered. Again and again in the days that followed, the man on the red horse and the lonesome little house with the barred window returned to his mind.

In the book of Revelation, chapter 6, verse 4, Jamie had read about a man on a red horse as a symbol of swords and killing and an end to peace.

He remembered the Separate preachers who had been jailed in Spotsylvania County the year before. Was *that* where the new road he had taken was to lead him—into jail? Barred windows, locked doors—Jamie had never shaken off his horror of these. *If my time should come, would I have the courage to choose jail rather than freedom?*

When he came to that point, Jamie smiled. *It's preachers they jail, not ordinary folk like me,* he reminded himself.

Jamie's two special friends had committed their lives to the cause which had now become all-important to him.

"There's to be services at Fincastle's next Saturday night," Tom Buck announced.

"Aye," McRae chimed in, "Brother Pickett is coming back to preach again, as he promised."

Announcement of a preaching service was good news to the Separates on Smith's Creek. Farm families worked hard all day Saturday so the chores could be finished early. Boys in starched jeans, girls in clean gingham walked or rode with their parents to Nathan Fincastle's house. Long before sundown the sandy front yard was crowded with wagons and horses. Men and women, their faces tired but eager, sat on the porch, on the steps, on the seats of wagons. Youngsters chased one another or stood and talked as they waited for the coming of the preacher.

Looking at them, Jamie felt that he could see into their hearts. He knew that many of them were reaching out for something they could not name, just as he himself had done. They wanted to know that there was a good God who loved them and cared what happened to them. Jamie prayed that God would put the right words on the preacher's tongue.

But John Pickett did not come. Sundown, early candle-light, late candlelight—still the people sat on the porch straining their eyes up the dark road.

"It is not like him," McRae kept muttering.

"No," agreed Fincastle, "he's generally punctual to his appointments."

"Let's not give up hope," encouraged Jamie. "Perhaps he lodged this night on the other side of Massanutten Mountain, planning to ride over early on the Lord's Day morning."

Gloomily the little congregation scattered. After milking time the next morning, they gathered again.

Still John Pickett did not ride down the slopes from the east.

Several men huddled in a back room.

"We cannot disappoint the people," said McRae.

"Then what's to be done?" demanded Tom. "Who among us can preach?"

Nathan Fincastle cleared his throat. Slowly he turned and looked Jamie squarely in the eye.

"Aye, 'tis the truth!" cried McRae. "A man with wit enough to keep school and write verse surely has wit enough to preach."

Jamie's heart skipped a little hornpipe of its own. "Me?" he squeaked. "A new convert?"

"Who else?" challenged Tom.

Solemnly then the four men knelt and begged God's help for the one of them who had been appointed to preach.

It was sultry summer noon before they emerged and

walked to the front room. A record crowd filled even the door and windows.

" 'O sing unto the Lord'!" recited Tom Buck, the singing master. "Let's join hearts and voices in Dr. Watts's hymn, 'Let Me but Hear My Saviour Say'!"

Eager tongues—some trained, some untutored—followed Tom as he lined out each stanza. Then Nathan Fincastle led in prayer.

Now it was Jamie's turn. His fingers fumbled for John's Gospel, chapter 3, verse 3. In trembling tones he read, " 'Except a man be born again, he cannot see the kingdom of God.' "

Gradually he realized that he was not afraid any more. The people watching him so trustingly were his friends. He had a splendid truth to share with them. Sentences tumbled out as Jamie dared every hearer to turn his whole life over to Jesus Christ, to walk a new road with him—to become a new person by God's power.

"Jesus Christ is the way you must walk in," urged Jamie. "Jesus Christ is the truth you must believe in. Jesus Christ is the possessor of that spiritual life you must share in if ever you are to see the kingdom of God."

"Hey, you old sailor," whooped Tom afterward, "you were speaking under so full a gale that I felt more sure of my faith than ever before. And hark you . . ." He dropped his voice. "Have you never heard Pickett read from somewhere in the Bible, 'The Lord will raise up unto thee a Prophet from the midst of thee, of thy brethren'?" He winked. "You're the man, Jemmy, you're the man!"

Jamie smiled and shook his head. Yet, he could not deny a strange satisfaction in having preached that day. He accepted several invitations to speak in houses throughout the settlement. *Shall I not work as hard for the good of my friends,* he argued with himself, *as I have worked to lead them in vanity?*

Often during the next month he found his mind returning to Tom's words. If indeed "so full a gale" had blown through his lips, it was God's doing, not his. Was God indeed calling him to be a preacher to his people?

Jamie prayed and thought—and prayed again.

At last he knew. *Aye, Lord,* he promised, *I'll be thy vessel of grace to steer for glory. Thine be the gale, and I'll trim my sails to catch it.* And with the certainty of his call, Jamie felt renewed power in his sermons.

"Brother Pickett has recovered," reported McRae after hearing Jamie preach one day. "He was sick—that's why he missed services at Fincastle's. Now he's to preach at Captain Thomas McClanahan's on Saturday and at Colonel Easom's on Sunday."

"And where are these places?" asked Jamie.

"In the northern part of Culpeper County. Will you ride over with Tom and me?"

Culpeper! Jamie smelled trouble.

"Isn't that Parson Meldrum's parish?" he asked.

"Aye, and we may have a merry time," warned McRae. "Parson Meldrum is touchy about any church services in that parish save his own in the Established Church."

The three friends saddled and rode away eastward— over Massanutten Mountain, across the South Fork of the Shenandoah, over Blue Ridge Mountain, and into Culpeper County.

A large crowd had gathered in Captain McClanahan's spacious parlor when the three friends from Smith's Creek arrived. As he took his seat Jamie sensed the same warm spirit of friendliness that he always felt when he mingled with the Separates in their services.

Then suddenly warmth and friendliness vanished from the room. There was a commotion at the door. Parson Meldrum strode in. With him were three stern-faced men.

"They're magistrates," whispered Tom. "Squire Slaughter, Squire Arnold, and Squire Strother."

"And, I doubt not, they're members of the Established Church?" inquired Jamie.

Tom nodded. "Faithful pillars of Meldrum's parish."

The parson made a great show of having his chair set squarely in front of the preacher, and only about ten feet away. He whipped out pen and paper, obviously planning to take notes.

Poor John Pickett! Jamie feared that the unfriendly

visitors had already unnerved him. His hands trembled as he opened his Bible.

During the sermon Parson Meldrum scribbled away. Jamie nudged Tom, then edged closer to the chair. He blinked to see the half-truths and twisted phrases with which the parson was covering his paper.

Pickett finished his sermon.

Meldrum held up his hand for silence. "Now!" He shot a look over his shoulder at the three magistrates. "Now, sir, you have proven yourself to be a schismatic and a broacher of false doctrines. Why, what diabolical error is this, to say that every man is free to approach God in any outlandish way he chooses!"

Pickett gasped. "I only said that—I mean—a man should be free—" He stopped.

"Out, New Light! You said it matters not, even though a man in his so-called freedom believe a lie." The parson glanced triumphantly at his parishioners, who smiled and nodded in return.

"Sir!" It was a new voice—Jamie's.

"I have eyes to see and ears to hear as well as you. It does no good for you to charge Mr. Pickett with such remarks, for he said them not."

Parson Meldrum's eyes opened wide. He swung around majestically in his armchair.

"Well! 'Out of the mouths of babes,' saith the Scriptures. And no doubt this boy of tender years thinks to best *me* in debate, for that his eloquent words are trimmed with a Scottish burr!"

Titters came from behind. But Jamie calmly picked up another chair and placed it beside the parson's. Easing himself down with the dignity of a judge, he announced, "I am determined to argue the point with you from end to end."

And argue it they did.

Like a skilled diplomat, Jamie at first ferreted out questions on which they could agree—questions about God, about the Scriptures, about man and his needs. Silently he gave thanks for his early training in the Bible and in the catechism.

"We must confess," reasoned Jamie, "that all a man may do can never please God, unless that man has faith in God—aye?"

"Oh, perhaps that's near enough the truth," conceded Meldrum. "But the doctrine of faith may admit of a different construction."

"Indeed!" Jamie ransacked his memory. "How can it be any different when the book of Hebrews says, 'Without faith it is impossible to please him'—that is, to please God?

"And how can you, of all men, seek another meaning when we read in the articles of religion for your own Established Church, 'All works, done before the grace of God and inspiration of the Spirit, are not well pleasing to

God, inasmuch as they have not the nature of faith in them'?"

Meldrum ran his finger around his collar. As Jamie continued to track him down with truth, he became more and more upset. Squire Arnold and other worried-faced members of the Established Church leaned forward and whispered in his ears apt Bible verses and ideas for arguments.

"Will you agree, then," pursued Jamie, "that no man can truly believe for another? That every man must have an inner liberty to make his own peace with God?"

"Of course!" snorted the ruffled minister. "Who could dispute such an evident truth?"

John Pickett grinned to see the trap that Jamie had laid. "How can you now confess it to be truth?" he burst out. "When I said it in different words, you called it error—and diabolical error, at that."

Parson Meldrum opened his mouth—and let it drop shut again in fuming silence. His eyes darted angrily from one Separate to the other.

Jamie blithely arose and stepped toward Squire Arnold. "Your worship, 'tis plain the dispute between the parson and myself is ended. If you are disposed to argue the subject over again, I am willing."

The magistrate stood, white-faced with rage. He shook a trembling forefinger under Jamie's nose.

"Infernal villain! Come no nigher me than that!"

Jamie smiled and bowed. As the parson and the magistrates hurried out, he turned to receive the congratulations of Pickett, Captain McClanahan and his family, and the two other visitors from Smith's Creek.

"He won't come back tomorrow," Captain McClanahan assured Jamie. "He must hold his own services. And I think he's had enough of arguments, anyway."

On Sunday the worshipers gathered in the shade of Colonel Easom's trees. No parson appeared, sure enough. But Squire Arnold saw to it that the Separates did not meet in peace.

Many slaves were included in the congregation. Suddenly some of them began to moan and to shout the age-old cry of warning: "Run, run! The patrolers are a-coming!"

The very thought of slavery appalled Jamie's freeborn soul. Now he stared with even more disgust to see the attack of the patrolers, who were supposed to keep all slaves in check.

Eyes shone white in frightened faces as men, women, and children were yanked up and shoved back toward their cabins. A few boys who ran were chased and whipped unmercifully.

Black, white, or speckled like a unicorn fish, mused Jamie, *a man should be free to worship God. I like not the way of things in Culpeper County. And God help any Separate who is tried before Squire Arnold's bench!*

10

A Ride to Carolina

Together the three Separates from Smith's Creek rode down the western slope of Massanutten Mountain. Together they turned homeward from the services they had attended in Culpeper County. But together they could not agree as they talked.

"I do not see," insisted Jamie Ireland, "why I should be baptized again. I am already a Separate; I believe a man can and should serve God separate from the Established Church. Why should I become a Separate *Baptist?*"

"Well," sighed Tom Buck, "I can't say I really know much about it. And I couldn't begin to try to win an argument with *you*. But I dare you to read your Bible on the subject."

"Aye, lad!" chimed in McRae. "Take not our word for it—or John Pickett's either. Read it for yourself."

And so Jamie again spent his mornings on the slope of
Massanutten, Bible in hand, seeking to learn what God
would have him do. Hints of fall sharpened the summer
air before he announced one Sunday, " 'Tis true, my
friends! I understand now from reading God's Word
that a believer should show his faith by being baptized."

The little group on Smith's Creek had a lively meeting
that day as they gave thanks for the oneness of belief they
now knew.

"But now we have another problem." Tom Buck
spoke for the group. "You should be our preacher,
Jemmy; that's plain. If you were baptized and licensed to
preach, then you could baptize the rest of us. But there
isn't a single Separate Baptist preacher to baptize you in
the whole colony of Virginia!"

"What about John Pickett?" protested Jamie.

"What about those five who were jailed in Spotsylvania
County last year?" added McRae.

"What about Elder Major up in Loudoun County, and
Elder Garrard?" inquired Nathan Fincastle.

Tom shook his head. "Brother Pickett and the men in
Spotsylvania are preachers, all right, but none of them are
truly ordained. And as for Major and Garrard, they are
Regular Baptists."

Jamie had quickly learned that there were two distinct
kinds of Baptists. They differed little in belief, but the
Separates were generally agreed to speak out more boldly

and warmly for God. That was why the believers on Smith's Creek wanted to become a Separate church.

Suddenly the little band of Christians learned of a possible solution to their problem.

"There's to be a meeting of Separates down in North Carolina," reported a visitor to the settlement. "Several Regular Baptist preachers from these parts plan to attend it, too."

" 'Tis a bonny opportunity!" cried Jamie. "When will they leave?"

"They left yesterday."

No more time for talk. With his usual dispatch Jamie crammed food into his mouth and luggage into his saddlebags. Away he rode to the southeast.

Up Massanutten, down into the South Fork Valley, up again over Blue Ridge, down into Culpeper County.

This seems familiar, thought Jamie as he entered at a canter the town of Culpeper Courthouse. *Buildings on the right, and in this field to the left there should be a . . .*

Yes, the little old house stood alone in the open field. Jamie realized then that he had ridden over two mountains, the same as in his dream. He jerked the left rein. Riding closer, he saw that the one little window in the ramshackle house was covered with iron grates.

It was the Culpeper County jail.

Sucking in his cheeks, Jamie rode on. The man on the

red horse, though, loomed ever larger in his thoughts.

"Can you tell me whither the Regular Baptist preachers have gone?" he shouted at a crossroads forge.

"They passed here yesterday afternoon," replied the blacksmith, "bound for Orange County."

Jamie set the tilt of his jaw. Sixty miles in a day and a half—yet he had gained only a half day on them. He urged his horse to a faster gait.

By nightfall it was plain that the horse could not continue such a pace. His back sagged with weariness and saddle sores. He wheezed and whinnied and fell into a shuffling walk.

"I know not what to do," Jamie confided that evening to a stranger who had allowed him lodging. "I would not want to miss the Baptist meeting."

"Baptist!" The host beamed. "Welcome, my brother; I'm one of 'em, too!"

"Can you not lend a horse, then, to the work of God's kingdom?"

The stranger shook his head. "I ain't got none. But don't you worry, young man; just rest ye here in my cabin. I'll rouse the neighborhood and find ye a mount somehow."

Rouse the neighborhood indeed! Next morning Jamie swung his leg over a prancing stallion—far superior to the one he had temporarily swapped for it.

On southward, trotting through forests sprinkled with

the first tints of autumn . . . splashing through creeks and even rivers . . . scarcely slowing down for shouted directions where two trails crossed . . . measuring off the miles that separated Jamie and his destination.

At the James River he hallooed for a boat. Whipping off his coat to use as a blinder, he led the skittish stallion into the tiny craft. *Quite a comedown from a whaler,* he decided with a silent chuckle as he paid the teen-ager who had rowed him across the broad stream.

Twilight was falling over Amelia County as Jamie pulled up near the windows of a large wayside house. He listened. The preaching he heard told him at once that the solitary part of his journey was now over.

It was Nathaniel Saunders who preached. Jamie met him afterward, and Richard Major and John Garrard, too—all being special delegates to the Separate association in North Carolina. They congratulated the young man who had ridden 150 miles, including 55 miles the last day, to catch up with them. Until late that night they chatted, as Jamie told them of his great adventure in search of God.

Early the next morning the little group assembled with their Baptist host for family worship on his front porch.

"Now, would ye look at them knock-kneed New Lights a-kneelin'!" The voice was thickened by liquor; its owner rode up with two friends he had just beaten in a horse race.

The man staggered up the steps. His speech became more and more profane as he saw that no one tried to answer him.

At last Brother Saunders had had enough. "Friend, you should not swear so; it's offensive to God and man."

The drunk charged across the porch, seized the un-resisting minister by the throat, and choked him till his face began to blacken.

It was Jamie who leaped to the attacker's side then, and unlocked his squeezing fingers one by one. Stout words in a broad Scots brogue, coupled with gestures by sinewy fists, at last sent him and his cronies on their way.

"God has blessed you with both a quick mind and a quick body," observed Brother Garrard as the little party of preachers rode on southward. "I'm thinking you should join me in preaching at this next meetinghouse along the way."

The former schoolteacher's arguments did little good. All along the road the others insisted that he take the lead in every service.

They also helped Jamie by debating religious questions with him. Often they pretended to support false views, thus sharpening his own ideas by conflict.

One evening near the North Carolina border, Jamie sat on another porch with the now enlarged group of trav-elers. Gospel-hungry settlers gathered in the front yard.

Brother Garrard looked at the deepening shadows. "Is it not time for worship to begin?"

"Aye, sir," agreed Jamie, "and I wish the preacher would take his place."

"You are the preacher, sir."

Jamie shook his head. "I am unprepared."

The gray-haired minister smiled. "You must remember what old Paul told young Timothy: 'Preach the word; be instant in season, out of season.'"

Jamie frowned. "God has not laid it upon me that I should be the one to preach tonight; else would I not hesitate."

His eyes twinkling, Brother Garrard leaned forward and gave Jamie a light slap between the shoulder blades. "Now *I* have laid it upon you, boy. Get up and preach!"

From then on Jamie did not argue. He gladly took every opportunity to share the faith that he had found.

Oaks and maples flamed on the hills when Jamie and his friends at last reached Sandy Creek, North Carolina. Crowded days followed, as Separates from three colonies conducted their matters of business. In fact, the schedule became so crowded that no one had time to baptize Jamie!

"Can we not frame some plan?" asked Shubal Stearns in his New England twang. (Jamie had quickly learned that the little old pastor at Sandy Creek always spoke with wisdom and authority.)

"Some of the brethren," continued Stearns, "plan to ride home with Colonel Samuel Harris, who has just been ordained. Would it not be fitting that young Brother Ireland, his fellow Virginian, become the first person baptized by Colonel Harris?"

And thus they worked it out. Twelve ministers rode northward across the border into Pittsylvania County. On the way Jamie learned what a distinguished gentleman would officiate at his baptism. "He commanded Fort Mayo and even served in the legislature—and that while scarce thirty!"

Jamie looked longingly at the magnificent church building on Dan River near Colonel Harris' home. Never before had he seen such a fine meeting place—for any except the Established Church.

"It was to have been his own new mansion," explained Brother Garrard. "Then when he found the Lord, he stayed in his old house and made this the house of God."

For three days the Baptists held meetings. On Sunday, as a grand climax, they scheduled five sermons for the morning service, beginning at eight o'clock.

Jamie was to preach fifth. The fourth man struck a shoal in his sermon, however. As he wandered in more and more confusion, Jamie gently tugged at his coattails. He gratefully sat down and let the fifth message begin.

Yet another sermon came after lunch, as Jamie's coach

in preaching, Brother Garrard, explained the doctrine and practice of baptism. Then Colonel Harris led Jamie just past the shallows of Dan River. Reverently they portrayed in water how the Lord Jesus had been buried in earth and raised again.

On Monday the eleven other ministers signed a paper that gave Jamie full license to preach. Several also persuaded him to speak at various places on his homeward trip. Away he rode on his borrowed horse, swapped it again in due time for his own nag, and so made the long journey back to Smith's Creek.

"Here's a prophet *with* honor among his own people!" proclaimed Tom Buck as the little would-be church came together. "Now you can stay among us again—as preacher instead of teacher."

Jamie squinted as he thought of the red horse in the dream. "Maybe, old friend—maybe."

11

"I Choose Freedom!"

The journey began harmlessly enough. Jamie Ireland replied to a call for help from Colonel Harris, the preacher who had baptized him.

"Can you meet me and other brethren on November 12," ran the message, "to help organize a church at Carter's Run in Fauquier County?"

Over Massanutten, across South Fork, over Blue Ridge rode Jamie as he had in his dream. He spent the night with Colonel Tipton in Culpeper County.

"Stop again and preach for us on your way back," requested Colonel Tipton.

Jamie smiled and shook his head. "I would make no promise that I could not keep." Then he told his dream about the man on the red horse, also about his arguments with the parson and magistrates.

The colonel looked grave. "All I ask, then, is that you stop and preach here if you can."

It was a happy reunion at Carter's Run. Colonel Harris greeted Jamie with the warmth of an older brother, as did John Pickett and others whom he knew. On the day appointed, they established a church with thirty members.

After observing the Lord's Supper with the new church, Jamie got an early start on his homeward trip. He had another pleasant reunion that evening with the McClanahan family.

Captain McClanahan, however, led Jamie into a corner away from the fire. "Parson Meldrum hasn't forgiven you for besting him in this very room," he warned. "Neither have the magistrates. We've hoped you would preach over at Mr. Manifa's tomorrow. But word has come that if you do, Squire Strother and Squire Slaughter will cast you into jail."

Late into the cool November night Jamie lay awake between two featherbeds. *Count the cost! Count the cost!* The warning Bible words seemed to drum in his brain. He had once left the dearest places and people he knew rather than risk losing his precious freedom. Was it worth the price to go ahead and preach this one time?

By morning Jamie knew the answer. "I have ventured all upon God," he announced to the captain. "Should I not suffer all for him?"

Mrs. McClanahan hurried to get all the children washed and dressed. "The least we can do is to stand by you, Brother Ireland," she explained.

After a short ride the little group arrived at the Manifas' house. Mr. Manifa scurried out to meet them, twisting his hands.

"Sir, I have been warned," he blurted out. "You'll be arrested and fined if you preach today. Everyone who attends the service will be fined. And I'll be fined *twenty pounds* for letting you preach in my house!"

He paused and gnawed his lip. "Yet—yet—don't flinch from your duty—" and then under his breath, "—if you think it a duty."

Jamie dismounted and laid a calming hand on Mr. Manifa's shoulder. "Dear friend, will you not show me the line of your land?"

The agitated landowner blinked for a moment. "There," he said at length, pointing. "There along the edge of those trees, and running to the stone marker by the road."

The day was crisp but sunny. "Let us worship the God of all the earth even here in his open fields," suggested Jamie. "Mr. Manifa, may we borrow a table from your house?"

Under Jamie's direction the table was brought and placed squarely on the boundary line—two legs standing on each side. "You see?" he explained to his quaking

Jamie heard a rustling in the woods.

host. "I will not preach on your property any more than on another's."

Jamie smiled as he mounted the table. He remembered well what he had done the last time he had stood on a table. Now he brought out his pocket Bible and preached as if he might never get the chance to do so again.

The sermon ended with a prayer. Just before the amen Jamie heard a rustling in the woods. He did not open his eyes until he felt fingers seizing his coat collar.

Two surly sheriffs forced him down off the table. Several other men walked out from under the trees. Among them Jamie recognized Squire Strother, Squire Slaughter, and Squire Arnold.

He felt a shiver of panic and almost bolted. Then his self-control took over. He turned to face the magistrates.

"What are you doing here with all these people?" demanded Squire Strother.

"Preaching the gospel of Christ to them."

"Who gave you authority to do so?" asked Squire Slaughter.

"He who is the Author of the gospel—has He not the right to give me authority?"

Squire Arnold spewed out an oath. "Villain, have you any human authority to preach?"

Jamie brought out his license. The magistrates passed it from hand to hand. "We see no bishop's name here," they sneered.

Then they came to the point. "Either give your bond not to teach, preach, or exhort in Culpeper County for twelve months and a day—or else go to jail."

" 'Tis no hard choice," pronounced Jamie. "I choose freedom."

The magistrates grinned and nodded at the sheriffs, then turned back toward Jamie. "There's a sensible rascal! Come along, now, to sign your bond."

Jamie shook his head. "You understand me not, your worships. I choose freedom—freedom to worship God and speak in his name when and as I will, even though for this freedom I go to jail."

Pompously the squires moved a few steps away, leaving him in the custody of the sheriffs.

"Friends and neighbors," declaimed Squire Strother, "we could have the law on every one of you, too. But there stands this preacher on one side, and we on the other. If you will confess, by coming over to our side, that you have been deceived by him, we'll take no action."

Silence.

Then the Separates to a man—even trembling Mr. Manifa—moved closer to Jamie.

Captain McClanahan was the spokesman. "You do wrong, your worships, law or no law. We have heard nothing today but the gospel of Christ. If we haven't enough money to pay our fines, we're willing to go to jail also."

Squire Strother snorted. He and his fellow magistrates said not a word more as they turned to lead Jamie away.

After the ride to Culpeper Courthouse, Jamie signed a bond promising to appear at the next court day—three days later. The McClanahans, the Tiptons, Colonel Easom and his family, and other Separate friends in the county encouraged him and promised all the help they could muster.

It was not enough. Strother, Arnold, Slaughter, and eight of their colleagues tried the case. They browbeat Jamie when he took the witness stand. They called him names and made fun of him, to the merriment of a packed courtroom.

"Hold your tongue!" they cried when Jamie tried to turn even this unlikely time into an opportunity to tell what he believed. "You're nauseating everybody with such diabolical doctrines!"

Silently Jamie set his stubborn chin. As sentence was about to be pronounced, he whispered to Captain Mc-Clanahan, "Will you give my poor horse a home for the night, and ask me at the jail tomorrow what to do next?"

For he knew well what the verdict would be. The eleven magistrates were determined to make an example of him.

By court order the sheriffs paraded him down the street

toward the little old house that he remembered so clearly from his dream.

"Radical!"

"Rabble-rouser!"

"Church-hater!"

So shouted the people as they straggled beside and behind him. Harsher words than these, along with occasional sticks and rocks, were flung in his direction. He found it hard to duck and still maintain the calm dignity he had hoped to show.

Panic almost struck again when the prison door creaked open. Dirt and garbage strewed the floor of the one room. Light came only from the tiny barred window. No furniture stood in the bleak cell. No fire crackled in its broken-down grate. And in one corner crouched a red-haired giant who glared wildly toward the door.

"In with you!" grunted a sheriff, giving Jamie a shove. The door swung shut—just in time to block a new volley of stones.

Jamie leaned against the heavy planks and squinted in the half-light. The huge redhead never relaxed his piercing gaze.

"An' what might you be doin' that they thry to kill you even on the way to jail?" he demanded. The gravelly voice hinted of that faraway country which bore the same name as Jamie Ireland's family.

The slender young man shook his head. "I've done

nothing except tell them the truth about God," he said.

"The thruth!" Suspicion gleamed in the fiery eyes. "You wouldn't be one of these heretics, now would you?"

Jamie shrugged. "I know not what you would call a heretic."

The other prisoner spat. "By the saints' eyeballs, that Brandon Donahoo should be locked in with a hell-bound heretic!"

Jamie decided to ignore this statement, except for the name. "I'm called James Ireland," he volunteered, "late of Edinburgh. In what part of old Ireland do the Dona-hoos live?"

"Killorglin," muttered Brandon. "County Kerry." Then he would say no more.

November's early nightfall left the room almost totally dark. People of Culpeper Courthouse kept on throwing rocks, sticks, and filth. Some of this at first whizzed through the bars, then spattered against the crude shutters after the jailer swung them into place. Cursing and name-calling continued far into the night.

At last things became more quiet.

Jamie could not bring himself to lie on the slimy black floor. He did finally sit down in the opposite corner from Brandon Donahoo, and gingerly leaned back against the rough walls.

He was not sure whether he slept briefly or only closed

Donahoo wheeled around, a brick in either hand.

his eyes. Either way, it was a scraping noise that caused
him to open them again. Adjusted now to the dimness,
they could make out a dark shape near the fireless
hearth.

It was the imprisoned Irishman. With elaborate care
he was working loose the crumbly bricks. His scheme
seemed simple: remove enough of the hearth to accom-
modate those broad shoulders, then squeeze out between
the underpinnings of the tumbledown house that served
as a jail.

Suddenly Jamie's eyes opened wider.

They'll blame me, he realized. *"If the man could have
escaped unaided before," they'll claim, "why did he not
do it?"*

Cold sweat chilled Jamie's forehead. Aiding an escapee
might be a serious matter—maybe even a hanging matter.

"Wheesht!" whispered Jamie. "That will do you no
good."

Brandon Donahoo wheeled around, a brick in either
hand. "Will you lave me alone?"

"Nay, friend," persisted Jamie. "I'll rouse the jailer if
you will not stop."

Donahoo's eyes narrowed to slits of fury. "I'll kill
you," he snarled. "Sure, an' I'll kill you if I die for it!" He
lurched toward Jamie, weaponed hands raised.

Jamie's mind skipped like a cornered mouse. All his
skill in boxing could not stop a burly peasant a foot taller

and armed with jagged bricks—especially when near-madness gleamed from his eyes.

"Come, come, now, you misunderstood me," he gasped. "I am not against finding the way to freedom. But will you not put it off a bit?"

The giant paused, his face still twisted by murderous rage.

Jamie smiled and held out his open hands. "I'll try to be your friend in every respect."

Brandon grudgingly dropped the bricks. Belching out a string of curses, he stumbled back toward his corner and flopped onto a grimy cowhide mat, face down.

Jamie's breathing eased. *But I dare not close my eyes,* he decided.

12
A Time to Fight

Daybreak brought the jailer, with salt pork, dry bread, and water—breakfast for two prisoners. Brandon wolfed his like a starved and chained beast. Jamie also ate quickly, as usual, but found even the scanty provisions hard to choke down. And the greasy tankard of luke-warm water did not begin to quench his thirst after eating the salty meat.

Brandon now began to alternate pacing the cell and stretching out on his filthy cowhide. Occasionally he shot black looks at his fellow captive.

Jamie held his pocket Bible to the morning light that filtered through the bars. Somehow he found little comfort as he tried to read. *If God has truly called me to serve him, why did he let this happen? And if he has not . . .*

Along with a puny lunch the jailer brought in a reeling

116

drunkard. "It's right handy at times," he remarked with a smirk, "being jailer as well as tavernkeeper. I always know what to do with guests I can't manage. Here, bishop, no doubt you'll convert him!"

The new inmate staggered toward Jamie. "Convert me, will ye? Take that!"

He was so far gone that Jamie had no difficulty in fending his blows. What he did next was no improvement, however, as he became violently sick beside the partly dismantled fireplace.

Jamie cleared his throat repeatedly as he tried to stick his nose as far out the window as possible. *If God has not called me to preach,* he bitterly wondered again, *what in the name of sin am I doing here?*

It was late afternoon before Captain McClanahan arrived. "Your horse is thriving, Brother Ireland," he announced. "How is it with you?"

Jamie shook his head. "No good. Will you be so kind as to bring the papers and witnesses I need, so as to sign my bond and get me out of this hellhole?"

The captain raised his eyebrows. "Well . . . all right, if that's what you want."

At length he returned with the jailer and two others. He showed Jamie the document that promised no preaching in Culpeper County for a year and a day.

As Jamie picked up a quill, an old, old scene suddenly darted into his mind. A faded carpet . . . shelves of lawbooks . . . a deep Scottish voice: "Try to remember—fight when you must, but always test yourself: 'Is this really a time to fight, or no?' 'Tis all I ask."

'Tis a time to fight, cried Jamie's conscience, *when men have no liberty to worship! God needs a champion this day to fight for freedom.*

"I must fight!" he blurted aloud.

"What?" Captain McClanahan and the other men looked puzzled.

Jamie smiled. "I mean, I must not sign this paper. Sorry I am that I troubled you to come."

Then it was the captain's turn to smile. "No trouble, young man, no trouble. I'm just glad you changed your mind." He glanced around the dingy room. "But seems to me you need some things, if you choose to stay here."

Jamie nodded. "Wood, especially—if that grate will still bear a fire. I would not worry about anything else till tomorrow; 'tis too late."

The young minister chuckled to see Captain McClanahan coming back a third time that evening and directing a servant who unloaded logs and kindling. A fire would lift some of the damp chill—and would also stop Brandon Donahoo from picking out any more bricks for awhile.

Despite the fire, the second night was even less comfortable than the first. A drizzling rain ushered in the first really cold weather of the fall. The jail door missed meeting the sill by three inches, and November gales whistled in. Cracks in the shoddily built walls and warped shutters made the whole prison seem almost like a sieve.

The other two prisoners made no sound except for grunts and moans. Jamie noticed again that Brandon Donahoo lay on his stomach or side, never touching his back to the cowhide.

Jamie hunched his body to conserve all possible heat. He hugged his knees, silently thanking God that he was still almost as small and agile as the cabin boy who had kept warm that same way during many an Arctic night.

Brandon stayed in his corner, so Jamie risked a few catnaps.

His eyes were bleary and his joints stiff when grey dawn appeared. Yet, new assurance came as he opened his Bible and read the promise of his Master: "If ye continue in my word, then are ye my disciples indeed; and ye shall know the truth, and the truth shall make you free."

I'll continue to be God's champion, pledged Jamie. *God has shown me his truth, and I am free. It matters not that I am behind bars.*

After breakfast the jailer released the now-sobered drunk. A more welcome visitor was Captain McClanahan, who came again as he had promised.

"A bed and bedding, a table and chair, and a candle

and candlestick are what I chiefly need," Jamie listed.
"Also a new supply of firewood." He hesitated, then
continued. "And could your gentle wife make me even a
wee meat pie, as she so well knows how?"

"Of course, of course!" boomed the captain. "I should
have thought sooner that jail fare would be little to your
liking."

The weather cleared in the afternoon, and Jamie
noticed the usual number of people up and down the
street. He had an idea.

" 'Ho, every one that thirsteth, come ye to the waters,' "
he trumpeted through the bars. " 'And he that hath no
money; come ye, buy, and eat; yea, come, buy wine and
milk without money and without price.' "

Several turned and walked closer. A few curious
youngsters lounged just outside the window, hands on
hips.

Having attracted attention with his quotation from the
prophet Isaiah, Jamie launched into a forceful sermon. A
few people laughed and eased away—but more stopped
to listen as they passed. The crowd grew rapidly.

"Yes, God offers freely to every man the cup of salvation and the milk of the Word. Taste, and see that the
Lord is good! Trust his grace and love, and know that his
service is perfect freedom!"

Jamie fancied that he saw signs of genuine interest on
two or three faces, when all at once another sound echoed

"Come ye, buy and eat!" trumpeted Jamie through the bars.

louder than his preaching. Four mounted men charged down the street, scattering the congregation. A few luckless ones were knocked down and bruised by flying hoofs.

Squire Arnold was one of the riders. Another was Mr. Steward, the innkeeper. They shook clubs over the heads of the youngsters and warned them of worse treatment if they listened to the prisoner preach another time. And Jamie quivered to see several slaves stripped to their brown skins, tied up like dogs, and lashed till they howled.

"And you, sirrah," screeched Squire Arnold, "you'll find yourself locked up in total darkness if ever you presume to do such a thing again."

That night Jamie snuggled into his comfortable rented bed. *'Tis easy to see that just a little of God's truth turns the world upside down in Culpeper County,* he mused. *I must not fail to give them more of it.*

Brandon groaned in his sleep. He rolled from his side onto his stomach.

For the first time Jamie began to think seriously about the sullen Irishman. *How can I do him good?* Jamie fell asleep turning that problem over in his mind.

Next morning he sneaked a closer look at Brandon— and at Brandon's clothes. Both nose and eyes told Jamie that the man was filthy. A constant scratching hinted strongly that he was not the only inhabitant of his corner.

Yet, Jamie observed that both of Brandon's long-tailed shirts were of fairly decent quality—under the grime.

"Mr. Donahoo," he began, "I pledged the other night to be your friend in every respect. Now let me say that I pity your cold berth on that bare cowhide." He paused and smiled. "Take no offense if I speak frankly; I'd like to make you more comfortable, but we must do some washing first."

"Lave me alone," grated Brandon. "I wouldn't be wantin' your sympathy."

"Come now," urged Jamie. "I ask only that we scrub your shirts and your person. Is that not a small price to pay for a warm bed?"

Brandon worked his jaws. At last he gave a curt nod and began to unbutton his shirt.

Jamie sucked in his breath sharply to see the Irishman's back. It was a furrowed field of red welts, running sores, and half-healed whip-cuts.

"No wonder you sleep on your belly!"

Brandon cursed. "Sure, an' it's no gentle tratement they give when one of his majesty's seven-year passengers thries to win his freedom."

So Donahoo was an indentured servant; Jamie had already suspected as much. Doubtless he had been shipped to Virginia for seven years as a punishment for crime, and was paying further penalties as a runaway.

Jamie hurried, with the help of soap and salve and

other supplies from his Separate friends, to make his fellow inmate more clean and more comfortable. The huge man said little, but Jamie thought his glances were less hostile. And he slipped on a clean shirt and crawled into bed that night like a docile child.

At dawn Jamie had another idea. "Mr. Donahoo, will you . . ."

"Brandon," the man gruffly corrected him.

"Aye, Brandon, then," chuckled the younger prisoner. "Will you join me in a wee service of worship?"

Brandon shrugged. "Do what you loike. I'll be listenin'."

Jamie began with a hymn—as if the congregation numbered one hundred rather than one. He was singing the fourth stanza when . . .

BOOOOM! CRRRAAAACK!

The explosion nearly deafened Jamie. Stinging smoke billowed up.

Together he and Brandon investigated.

"Gunpowder, by the saints' eyeballs!" Brandon stuck his head almost under the one plank in the floor which had been partly forced up by the blast. "They're thryin' to blow us up!"

Trying to kill me, Jamie grimly decided. *That was the corner where I sat until I got the chair and bed—and someone knew it well!*

13
Indian Pepper, Brimstone—and Poison

Thus the second attempt on Jamie's life ended in failure. Brandon, who himself had made the first try, became more and more indignant as he realized the intent of the explosion.

In another way also he showed that he now counted Jamie a friend. When the young minister would preach repeatedly (despite repeated threats), Mr. Steward and some of his cronies would throw things through the bars and actually reach in to punch Jamie's face. One day Brandon, growling in his throat, ran his trunklike red arm out through the grates and grabbed the nearest persecutor by the hair. Before Jamie could stop him, he had bashed the man's head against the bars and pulled in a handful of hair.

"Nay, nay!" reproved Jamie. "You must not."

Brandon repeated every word like a great poll-parrot.

Brandon snorted. "Sure, an' if you won't be takin' care of yourself, I'll be thryin' to take care of you."

As he shared Jamie's bed, as he shared the food Jamie's friends brought, as he shared the warmth of Jamie's fire, Brandon also began to share more of Jamie's beliefs.

Every morning they would hold their simple service of worship. "You should pray, too," prompted Jamie.

Brandon knotted his rusty eyebrows like a slow schoolboy. "I *think* I'm rememberin' how." Kneeling then as Jamie did, he began to pray. *"Pater . . ."* He screwed up his face again, then recalled another word. *"Pater noster, . . ."*

"Brandon, can you tell me what that means?" Jamie gently asked.

The ruddy giant shook his head.

"Then should you not pray in words you know, and so open up your real thoughts to God?"

Brandon looked blank. "How?"

"When I pray," instructed Jamie, "listen well. When I say aught to God that you agree with, tell God so in your heart."

He nodded, and they started their prayer time again. But so little had he understood that he repeated aloud like a great poll-parrot every word of Jamie's that he could grasp.

"Nay, dear friend," corrected Jamie, almost in despair. "God hears what you think; it is not necessary to speak.

When you get the knack of it, then will be time and plenty to pray aloud."

With such elementary teaching Jamie led his backward companion to learn more about the ways of God with men, about what Christ expects of his true followers. Gradually Brandon seemed to pick up speed in his schooling. Every day he surprised his teacher with some new understanding.

November gave way to December. The weather was unusually cold, and Jamie suffered, even with his warm bed and crackling fire. His Separate friends brought huge loads of wood, also food that nourished both prisoners far more than what the jailer supplied.

The jailer realized that his popular prisoner had an unusual amount of company. He decided to make the most of the situation. "Anybody who goes in," he ruled, "must go as a debtor entering debtors' prison, and come out only when the debt is paid."

Jamie gave him a look of contempt. "And what is the debt?"

"Four shillings, eight pence."

Some of Jamie's fellow believers could afford to pay such a fee. For others, Jamie paid it himself in order to enjoy their conversation.

The jailer also continued to harass Jamie with drunken rowdies, whom he allowed to visit free of charge. Many a night Jamie and Brandon had to subdue two or three who were in a fighting mood, or to endure the mock religion of one who had heard there was a preacher in the jail. Even to some of these, Jamie was able to witness. Several thanked him, when released, for starting their thoughts toward more important things in life.

The news spread through northern Virginia that another Separate was in prison. Interest glowed especially high because so many people knew Jamie or had heard of him.

Letters began to come—by Christmas, an average of almost one a day.

David Thomas, a learned Regular Baptist minister, wrote from Fauquier County. Jamie's heart thumped with renewed excitement as he read one paragraph in the letter:

"Brother, if by bearing the cross of Jesus Christ you can win one of the strongest of Satan's strongholds, no matter then how soon you die. And if you thus die for him, how would the glorious armies of the martyrs shout to see Ireland coming from a prison to reign with them in glory!"

"The strongest of Satan's strongholds" was a shrewd choice of words. Jamie continued to find it so as he persisted in preaching God's truth to the people of Culpeper County. Horseback riders still plowed through the crowds. Jamie was threatened with a public whipping every court day. Stones rattled on the bars, and vile-smelling liquids sloshed against them as he spoke.

Yet, the people came. From miles around they came to hear the preacher whose pulpit was a prison. And, so Jamie's friends reported, many of them boldly announced their faith in God.

With such encouragement, freedom's champion felt more sure than ever that he had found "a time to fight"—the greatest fight of his life. With a grand flourish he replied to his friends with letters headed "From My Palace in Culpeper."

The new year, however, brought new problems for Jamie. January of 1770 was still young when Brandon began to gasp and wheeze one night.

"What's the matter?" asked Jamie. Almost at the same instant, he too began to labor for breath.

"Brimstone!" choked Brandon. "Burning brimstone!" He leaped out of bed and began to paw the walls.

Jamie joined him in a desperate search for cracks. They jammed their noses against the crannies and frantically gulped in every available wisp of fresh air.

Before the foul sulphurous smoke cleared, both of them became miserably sick. "Sure, an' it's more than brimstone," gasped Brandon.

Jamie also wondered what made his nose and throat itch so maddeningly, along with the nausea caused by the overpowering rotten-egg smell. When dawn broke, the two grey-faced cellmates began their investigation.

It was Jamie who thought of looking under the ill-fitted door. Just outside he saw a little pile of ashes. Poking it with his pen-knife, he turned up several charred reddish pods.

"Indian pepper," explained Brandon. "Indian pepper, with brimstone stuffed inside. Why, a man would be dyin' if he snuffed much of that!"

Jamie mentally marked the third deliberate attempt to take his life. Nor was that the only time when killing smoke billowed into the jail. Every time the wind was right for several nights, he and Brandon knew to stand by their cracks in the wall or shutter.

"That rascal Steward is behind this," raged Colonel Tipton when he came to visit. "It was he and his friends who tried to blow you up, too, so I hear. Luckily they managed to collect only half a pound of gunpowder, or you might have been blown to flinders."

These new attacks drew Jamie and Brandon even closer together.

The Irishman now expressed an interest in Jamie's pocket Bible, from which he read aloud every day.

"Here, you may see it," offered Jamie.

The redhead glanced at it, fingered the binding, and handed it back.

"Can you not read?"

"Niver learned," he muttered.

"Do ye not know your *ABC*?"

"I've heard of it, but I can't say I'd be knowin' it if I met it on the strate," he confessed.

Dipping quill in ink, Jamie proceeded to draw an alphabet for his class of one. Uncertainly, but not too slowly, the huge man learned all twenty-six of the letters.

"Now you need a book of your own," announced Jamie. When Colonel Easom came to visit, Jamie gave him money to purchase a New Testament.

Brandon leafed through it proudly. "Niver had a book before in me loife!"

Jamie started him out with the small words that the apostle John liked so much to use in his Gospel. Then they moved on to other books—and read from the Old Testament in Jamie's Bible as well.

To the young schoolteacher's surprise, Brandon proved to have a good memory for words and sentences, once it was aroused. Jamie grinned to hear him quote passages that perfectly fit some of the serious talks they now began to have. *It will not be long,* Jamie exulted inwardly, *before you will find God as I have, my friend.*

And then, amid these signs of encouragement, came the greatest danger of all during Jamie Ireland's prison term.

It began with a fever that troubled him during the night. More than ever he realized that the supply of water was inadequate, but the jailer seemed unwilling to bring more.

The fever continued—not severe, but enough to make every night uncomfortable. "May I see a doctor?" he begged the jailer at last.

It seemed to Jamie, as he thought about it later, that the jailer was a little too eager to bring a doctor. A beefy-faced, coarse-voiced man, the doctor quickly brought out a bottle of black medicine.

"Just a little will do you little good," he rasped. "Take a long draught if you expect to rid yourself of that fever."

When he felt his forehead grow hot and his hands clammy that evening, Jamie uncorked the bottle and set it to his lips. The taste was vile, but he manfully swigged a third of the dark flask.

It was about half an hour later that he noticed the first twinge of pain. Then it began to squeeze his stomach like the arms of an octopus. Fiery shafts of agony shot through him from chest to hips. At the same time he felt more sick and dizzy than he had ever before felt in his twenty-two years.

"God, save me, or I die!" he groaned.

The worried Brandon mopped his sweat-beaded face and brought him a basin as it was needed. Yet the pain continued without ease. Jamie decided he now knew what a whale must feel like when sailors grind harpoons into its intestines.

At last the screams he could not stifle brought the jailer

running. "Do you need the doctor again?" he shouted.

"Not that doctor!" Jamie forced out the words between agonizing spasms. "He poisoned me—you and he—deny it not!"

"Ye spalpeen," thundered Brandon, "is it thrue or false?"

The jailer turned a shade paler. "I'll—I'll call another doctor," he muttered, and bolted.

Apparently it unnerved him that the latest scheme had not succeeded in murdering Jamie outright, for he did indeed bring a different doctor. This one, a dapper middle-aged man, confirmed Jamie's fears.

"It's poison, no doubt about it," he judged after considering the symptoms. "Take a sip of this sweet oil, prithee, and it may bring a little relief."

Sweet oil, Brandon's fumbling but earnest care as nurse, and wholesome foods prepared by worried Separate wives—these brought slow healing to Jamie's tortured insides. He did not recover completely, however, and the fever still dragged on every night. He began to wonder whether he could live until May, when his case was to be heard in court again.

14
Victory!

Snowy January, icy February, chilly March, and still Jamie's body felt like the ribs of a wreck washed by tides. Many times he had to lean on Brandon's treelike shoulders as he preached through the bars by sheer willpower.

Then one day the beefy-faced doctor came back, along with the jailer. "Your condition is alarming," the jailer stated.

(*As if I knew it not,* Jamie mused bitterly.)

"Therefore, it has been decided to move you to the doctor's home and there let you continue under house arrest, so he can care for your needs."

Jamie smiled grimly. "You think to find another chance to poison me, eh, doctor?"

"Humph!" The doctor shook his head. "One man's physic is another man's poison. I truly regret if my medicine did not cure you, but it's in my heart to do you good."

"Just keep it in your black heart!" snapped Jamie. "I will not come out."

The jailer glanced back as they walked toward the door. "We'll speak of this again."

By careful inquiries among his Separate friends, Jamie found what was behind his new plot.

"Why, it's some of your old companions over in Shenandoah County," explained Colonel Easom. "They've offered the jailer and that quack doctor a bribe of two hundred pounds to nurse you back to health."

Jamie was ready, then, when a committee headed by Harry Routon rode up to see him.

"Old friends, old friends, truly I appreciate your favors!" he saluted his former partners in play. "But I must uphold the honor of the cause for which I suffer. I can come out on no other terms."

Harry gloomily shook his head as the committee prepared to leave. "What good will it do anyone, Jemmy, if you kill yourself?"

What good indeed? Jamie thought he had at least a partial answer several days later.

It was court day. Wagonloads of farm families rumbled past the jail through the morning. By early afternoon many farmers had joined the usual crowds outside Jamie's cell. Even the tree that shadowed his window held many listeners—youngsters, for the most part, who wanted to get close enough to see and hear the prisoner who preached.

Jamie opened his Bible and read, forcing his weakened voice to ring clear above the noise of the crowd: " 'If the Son therefore shall make you free, ye shall be free indeed.' "

He looked out at his audience. He held up his arms. "What do you behold when you look at me? A prisoner? A man deprived of his freedom? No, I tell you that I am free, in a way that many of you know not. I have found my true freedom in God's Son of whom the Bible speaks."

His forefinger jabbed toward first one, then another of his hearers. "*You* are the prisoners—you, and you, and likewise you. Only as you bow your will to Christ can you drop your chains. I would that each of you might tell him in your heart, 'I do believe, I now believe in thee.' Tell him that you would be forgiven of your sins. Ask him to take the rudder of your life and guide it. Only then can you enter into the fellowship of our Lord and escape all bondage."

Jamie soon knew for sure that he had found the answer to Harry Routon's farewell question. Friends brought him reports of increasing conversions, both among those to whom he himself had preached, and among those in distant settlements who had heard of his brave fight.

How he chuckled to hear that Squire Arnold's own daughter Amy was among those who had turned to God after hearing him preach! The plucky fourteen-year-old had flouted her father's orders, hiked two miles, waded a creek with shoes and stockings in hand, and joined other boys and tomboy girls who climbed trees along the street, the better to see and hear the imprisoned preacher. Jamie had noticed that pretty little face peering through budding twigs, as he glanced above the crowd that completely blocked the roadway.

The singing, the praying, the Bible reading, the preaching lodged in Amy Arnold's young heart that day. Boldly she announced—at home and elsewhere—that she intended to be baptized as a Separate.

In another unexpected way Jamie returned good for evil to one of his persecutors. Mr. Steward, the innkeeper, was following his usual practice of heckling and insulting Jamie during a sermon one day. Then he turned to his cronies and bawled, "Who'll lend me ten shillings? I need to lay in more supplies before next court day."

Not a one of his companions could or would produce this small sum.

"Mr. Steward?"

The innkeeper turned and opened his eyes wide to see ten shillings glinting in the spring sunshine. They lay in Jamie's hand, stretched full length through the bars.

"You did not ask me for the loan," continued Jamie,

his eyes twinkling, "but here it is. I rest in your honesty;
you may return it when it suits you."

Two bright red spots flamed in Steward's cheeks. He
batted his eyes. Making an awkward bow, he scraped the
silver off into his own greasy hand and hurried away to
get his supplies.

Thereafter he was Jamie's friend. No more did he ride
his horse through the crowd. No more did he heckle;
indeed, he threatened and argued with those who still did
so. Many a day he and his wife persuaded the jailer to let
them have the key, and they sat and talked with Jamie by
the hour. He apologized repeatedly for his part in the
gunpowder and brimstone plots.

And Brandon Donahoo, of course, was still another
enemy whom Jamie had won. He showed real concern
now over wrongs he had done, and over his need for God.
Night after night, as Jamie pretended to be asleep, he felt
his cellmate slip out of bed, saw him drop to those bare
red knees that stuck out below the nightshirt, and heard
him pray in his broken brogue that God would show him
the way to truth and light and freedom.

Jamie's health improved a little as April brought
violets to the Virginia hills. He had a plan now, but it
would take much doing before the grand jury hearing
scheduled for May. Accordingly, he talked things over
with several of his friends, and decided he had stayed in
jail long enough to prove his point. Papers were signed

pledging his return to Culpeper in a month's time, and the door swung open at last.

Brandon Donahoo wept like a child. "Sure, an' I've niver had such a friend!" he blubbered.

Jamie pushed his arm as far around the giant body as it would reach. "Jesus is your friend, Brandon. Serve him in truth and love, and he will never leave you, in this world or the next."

"But—but—will I niver be seein' you again?"

Jamie smiled. "Surely they will not jail you too much longer. If you can make your way to Smith's Creek in Shenandoah County, ask for me at the Jackmons' house. Happy I'll be to see you again."

With that, they parted.

Immediately Jamie asked Captain McClanahan for his nag—now fat and sleek from good food and little riding. Off they trotted to the north. Through Culpeper County and nearby Frederick County, freedom's champion rode, collecting signatures on a petition to have a Separate meetinghouse built at Culpeper Courthouse.

Then it was a long ride indeed—far down toward the sea, through dense forests, across the Rapidan, across the Mattaponi, across the Pamunkey, to the Capitol at Williamsburg.

Jamie had a momentary qualm as he realized that a warrant for his arrest on charges of assault might still be circulating among the British colonies. Then he squared his shoulders and marched into the red brick building to seek an audience with the British governor.

Norborne Berkeley, Lord Botetourt, received him graciously. "I see no reason why your wish should not be granted," he conceded, "*if*—if you follow the laws laid down for those who hold to other faiths. Such laws require written permission from a clergyman of the Established Church, given upon the passing of an examination in doctrines."

Jamie frowned, but remembered to thank Lord Botetourt for his courtesy. Then he set out to seek a parson.

"Off with you!" the first one dismissed him. "I have no time to hear a New Light say his prayers."

"I'm not the man you want," alibied the second. "Try Parson Prewitt on the other side of town."

Parson Prewitt was too sick, so his servant said, to be bothered.

Parson Tucker had pressing business that day in Yorktown.

Jamie doggedly branched out into James City County. At last, eight miles from Williamsburg, he found a country parson who grudgingly admitted that his beliefs were sound enough, and signed the necessary certificate. *To get well rid of me, I'll be bound!* Jamie chuckled.

Back to the Capitol to get the license signed by the governor, then back to Culpeper County for the trial.

Jamie waved the paper with the governor's signature.

Jamie grinned to see far more friends in the courtroom this time than the previous November. Indeed, there were now many more Separates in Culpeper as a result of his imprisonment. Mr. and Mrs. Tom Buck of Smith's Creek had also ridden across the mountains to bring him greetings and encouragement.

But the magistrates were there too, and a frowning Parson Meldrum, and a king's attorney who ranted as if his life depended on winning the case.

"Guilty or not guilty?" demanded the clerk.

"Not guilty!" cried Jamie. "If five hundred witnesses on my side will not be enough, I can produce a thousand."

Out of sheer love for suspense and surprise, Jamie let his foes build up their whole case before he reached inside his coat and dramatically held out the license signed by Lord Botetourt.

Squire Arnold's mouth fell open. Squire Slaughter scratched his wig. The king's attorney stammered. Parson Meldrum looked marlinspikes at Jamie.

In spite of the governor's license, however, the furious magistrates seemed determined to find some pretext to send Jamie back to jail.

The baffled young minister spoke over his shoulder to Captain McClanahan. " 'Tis plain you'll soon have the keeping of a horse again."

"Psst! Psst!"

It was Tom Buck, urgently leaning forward. "Jemmy, do you have any objection to hiring a lawyer?"

A lawyer! Jamie had not thought of this, since most lawyers had little sympathy with Separates. He quickly recalled, however, that one attorney named Bullett had seemed to listen with interest as he preached through the bars.

"Nay, Tom, I've no objection—if the lawyer will make good his case." He turned and spotted the man he wanted just two rows behind him. "Mr. Bullett, will you undertake my cause and insure success?"

The lawyer nodded, eager for the fray. "That is, for five pounds I will," he added.

"Done!" agreed Jamie.

Mr. Bullett immediately stepped forward and plunged into a long-winded argument with the magistrates, the king's attorney, and Parson Meldrum, who kept speaking up out of turn.

"Why, your worships," appealed Bullett, "you would prosecute this man upon laws that have had no existence since the accession to the throne of His Majesty William the Third in 1689. The Act of Toleration has made our colonial laws against Dissenters a dead letter these eighty years. You yourselves are subject to prosecution because of your false charges and illegal procedure!"

The magistrates were obviously caught. They muttered, passed notes back and forth, and held private arguments among themselves and with the king's attorney. Parson Meldrum leaned over the bar and officiously whispered bits of advice.

"Mr. Bullett," hissed Jamie in a stage whisper that carried across the room, "ask the court to let the parson and me argue the matter. If I cannot win my case, I'll go to prison as a volunteer!"

The crowd, now largely on Jamie's side, rocked with laughter.

"Order! Order in the court!" squalled the frustrated magistrates. But when quiet was restored, they still could find little answer to make.

Suddenly Squire Arnold stood up, slapped on his three-cornered hat, and stalked out. One by one the other magistrates followed him until the judicial bench was empty.

The clerk cleared his throat. "Will the defendant give his bond to come back when this case is called up again?"

Jamie feigned surprise with an impish stare. "This is the appointed time; let the court pursue its object now."

The clerk smiled foolishly. "Nevertheless, will the defendant give his word?"

Jamie knew the embarrassed squires would now leave him alone. He could afford to be generous. "I do so," he promised with a mock bow. Then he turned to receive the handshakes, hugs, and backslaps of his friends.

15

Freedom's Champion

And now Ireland's career as freedom's champion began in earnest. Until the meetinghouse could be built in Culpeper, the governor's license gave Separates the right to raise a brush arbor—a temporary shelter of poles and branches. This they did, and began to preach God's truth to the throngs who came.

Ireland himself traveled southeastward from Culpeper Courthouse on a missionary journey that took him almost all the way to Chesapeake Bay. Everywhere he met opposition.

"Knock him down!"

"Whip him out of town!"

"Let the parson answer his foul words!"

As he neared the sea, his opponents would bring sailors ashore and urge them to duck him from the yardarm of a

146

ship. He chuckled to think how little they knew about his familiar and fearless acquaintance with salt water.

But everywhere he also found friends, and those who opened their minds to his teaching. They begged the fiery little missionary to come back and tell them more about the way to freedom in God's service.

Now two hundred miles away from his friends at Smith's Creek, Ireland felt a yearning to go home. Slowly he returned, preaching as he went.

"Someone came and asked for you," the Jackmon family reported a few weeks later.

"What did he look like?"

"A great monster of a man," they replied, "with hair like glowing embers."

"Did he leave no message?" cried James Ireland.

"No."

And he never saw Brandon Donahoo again. *But I hope to meet him on the high street of heaven,* he told himself.

Meanwhile Ireland saw others who, like Brandon, needed to hear the story of God's Son. Up and down the creek bottoms, over the high mountains, into the hidden hollows he rode with a flaming message of freedom and forgiveness. For more than three decades he pounded the trails of what are now the border counties of Virginia and West Virginia. Berry's Gap, Woodstock, Stoverstown, Lost River, Luna's Creek, Dunkard Bottoms, Redstone, White House, Shirtee Creek, Cedar Creek . . . he lost count of the churches he founded and the people he baptized. One day he baptized fifty-two people in thirty-seven minutes!

He was not alone through those hard but happy years. In Fauquier County he met Jane Burgess and led her to find faith in God. He also led her to find happiness in becoming a preacher's wife. For eighteen years they made a Christian home for many children, many friends.

Jane Ireland died while still a young woman. James Ireland then courted and won Ann Pollard of Frederick County. She proved a faithful companion the rest of his days.

In all, nine little Irelands were born, and seven lived to be grown: James, Francis, Thomas, Letitia, Nancy, Jenny, Letty, William, and Lucinda. Delightful word pictures written by friends of the family show us twelve-year-old Nancy running to get fresh water for her father when he came in weary from a preaching tour . . . three-year-old William sitting near his father to share a cup of tea . . . seven-year-old Jenny speaking boldly in her father's defense at a time of trouble . . . eight-year-old Lucinda reading a poem her father wrote to show her how to act in school.

These were exciting years in America, as the colonies broke loose from their mother country. James Ireland, ever freedom's champion, used his poetic skill to celebrate the great event of 1776:

"Hail now, ye sons of liberty,
Behold thy constitution!
Despotic power and tyranny
Have seen their dissolution.

"Amidst the blessings we enjoy
From God the gracious giver,
Let gratitude our hearts employ,
To praise his name forever.

"Most gracious God, we thee adore,
Whose mercy faileth never;
Thy guardian care we now implore:
Be thou our King forever!"

Ireland's main concern, however, was making Christians, not making verse. He even traveled once as far as the wilderness of Kentucky, preaching along the way.

Like Job in Old Testament days, he reported, " 'I made a covenant with mine eyes.' Else I would scarce have returned to Virginia when such a bonny land beckoned me."

But all was not well with James Ireland during the long years of his ministry. He never quite recovered from the effects of his brutal treatment while in Culpeper jail. Becoming nauseated, feeling stings of pain in his stomach—these were a part of his very life.

Yet he did not spare himself. He traveled so far and preached so hard—often four times a day—that friends warned him he would soon die. Still he kept on, ever riding toward that next cove, that next settlement where people needed to hear God's truth.

In spite of pain and weakness, James Ireland's indomitable spirit remained sturdy. He never missed a morning leading his family in worship.

When he could no longer ride, his brothers in the ministry held preaching services in his home. Once he insisted on being propped up in a chair, and stoutheartedly preached himself.

One day Ireland began to wonder whether his children—or anyone else, for that matter—knew how God had led him through all the strange adventures of his venturesome life. He hired a secretary to scribble down the words that tumbled out between his pale lips—tales of Scotland, tales of the sea, tales of persecution in Culpeper jail.

More than once he lay back on his pillow and dictated, "I cannot take time to tell all about this, but must hasten on to other matters before I die."

And he had not quite finished his book when he quietly drew his last breath on May 5, 1806.

Freedom—Today

It seems strange that James Ireland is so largely unknown today, when he took such pains that this very thing should not happen. On his deathbed he dictated two hundred pages, crammed with events of his life.

Not that he wanted people to remember and glorify him; rather, his purpose was (in his own words) to tell "of the wonderful dealings of a gracious God." He dedicated his book to the "comfort and encouragement" of all true followers of his Lord.

But books, like people, can be forgotten. James Ireland's autobiography has been out of print for nearly a century and a half. Only a few copies exist today, most of these in sections of libraries reserved for rare books with crumbly yellow pages.

I picked up one of those dusty old books one day and began to leaf through it. Thus I discovered the lively lad known as Jamie Ireland and the fearless man he grew up to be. And I determined to bring James Ireland back to life, so that people may discover once again through his story "the wonderful dealings of a gracious God."

Here a detail or word of dialogue added, there two happenings telescoped into one, the name "Nathan Fincastle" supplied where Ireland's autobiography had merely "N. F."—these were almost the only types of changes needed. By far the bulk of the volume you are now reading is James Ireland's story, told just as James Ireland told it—and told with James Ireland's high purpose still in view.

For the struggle for freedom of conscience still goes on. Some battles are won, some lost.

Culpeper jail was at last torn down, and in its place rose a Baptist church—with "To the Memory of James Ireland" engraved on the bell in the steeple. But in many parts of the world, those who follow Jesus Christ today are called on to show the same kind of bravery that James Ireland showed two hundred years ago.

He was freedom's champion for his generation.

Who will be the champions now?